PRENTICE HALL
WRITING AND GRAMMAR

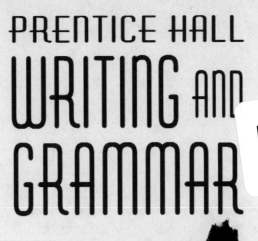

Standardized Test
Preparation Workbook

Teacher's Edition

Grade Six

PEARSON
Prentice Hall

Boston, Massachusetts,
Upper Saddle River, New Jersey

Copyright © by Pearson Education, Inc., publishing as Pearson Prentice Hall, Boston, Massachusetts, 02116. All rights reserved. Printed in the United States of America. This publication is protected by copyright, and permission should be obtained from the publisher prior to any prohibited reproduction, storage in a retrieval system, or transmission in any form or by any means, electronic, mechanical, photocopying, recording, or likewise. The publisher hereby grants permission to reproduce these pages, in part or in whole, for classroom use only, the number not to exceed the number of students in each class. Notice of copyright must appear on all copies. For information regarding permission(s), write to: Rights and Permissions Department, One Lake Street, Upper Saddle River, New Jersey 07458.

Pearson Prentice Hall™ is a trademark of Pearson Education, Inc.
Pearson® is a registered trademark of Pearson plc.
Prentice Hall® is a registered trademark of Pearson Education, Inc.

ISBN 0-13-361670-3

1 2 3 4 5 6 7 8 9 10   10 09 08 07 06

Contents

Responding to Writing Prompts

Standardized tests often include an essay writing section. Use these pages to plan and develop an essay in response to the following prompt.

Sample Writing Situation

> Writer Jane Yolen comments, "Anything I've experienced can find its way into one of my stories."
>
> Write an essay in which you describe an experience you have had that you think would make a good story. Provide the details of the experience, and explain why you think it would make a good story. Identify the types of readers who would like to read your story, and tell why.

Who is the audience? _____

_____

What is the purpose of your response? _____

_____

What is the format of your response? _____

_____

What three tasks are identified? _____

_____

_____

Prewriting

After you choose an experience, outline its key events on the timeline. For each event, identify the people involved and the setting.

To plan your introduction, jot down three characteristics of a good story.

_____

_____

_____

_____

_____

_____

Responding to Writing Prompts (continued)

Drafting

Write a one-sentence summary of your experience. Explain why this experience would make a good story according to the characteristics you have listed. Then, use these notes to help draft your introduction.

_____

_____

_____

_____

_____

Write an outline to plan your response. For each section of the essay, indicate what you will discuss.

1. Describe the experience

_____

_____

_____

_____

_____

_____

2. Explain why it would make a good story

_____

_____

_____

_____

_____

_____

Now write your essay on a separate sheet of paper.

Revising

Reread your essay to see if you have left out any important details. As you revise, make note of the changes you make.

Identify two details you can add to provide more information. Explain how each improves your essay.

Detail 1: _____

_____

_____

Detail 2: _____

_____

_____

Using the Writing Process to Respond to Writing Prompts

Standardized tests often require you to respond to writing prompts. Using the writing process will help you generate thoughtful, well-elaborated responses. Use these pages to plan and develop a response to the following prompt.

Sample Writing Situation

> While most people expect to spend time at school in classes required for graduation, many students enjoy participating in extra-curricular activities such as sports and clubs. In a letter to be included in a new student welcome packet, describe your own experiences in order to encourage others to get involved in such activities.

Who is the audience for your response? _____

_____

What is the purpose of your response? _____

_____

What is the format of your response? _____

_____

Prewriting

Identify some activities you have been involved in. For each, jot down two benefits of participating in the activity.

Activity: _____ Benefits: _____

Activity: _____ Benefits: _____

Activity: _____ Benefits: _____

Review your list and identify elements of participation that will appeal to new students.

_____

_____

_____

_____

_____

Place a check next to the organizational plan that suits your prewriting work.

☐ Discuss one activity and all it rewards.

☐ Address several activities and discuss a single benefit for each one.

Using the Writing Process to Respond to Writing Prompts (*continued*)

Drafting

Use the following lines to state your position. This main idea should go in your opening paragraph.

_____

_____

_____

_____

_____

Choose one point your essay will develop to support your position.

_____

_____

_____

For this point, identify two details that elaborate your idea.

Detail 1: _____

_____

_____

Detail 2: _____

_____

_____

Now, write your full letter on a separate sheet of paper. Use letter format, including date, greeting and closing. Make sure that you include examples or information that encourage students to join school-sponsored activities.

Revising

Your goal is to make the new students feel comfortable and welcome. Reread your letter, checking to see if the tone is friendly.

Note two places in your letter where you can make the language friendlier. Write the original sentences here.

_____

_____

_____

_____

Revise the sentences using the lines below.

_____

_____

_____

_____

Analyzing Strategy, Organization, and Style

Directions: Read the passage, and then answer the questions that follow. Mark the letter of your answer on a bubble sheet if your teacher provides one; otherwise, number from 1 to 6 on a separate sheet of paper, and write the letter of the correct answer next to each number.

(1) Saturday was the day of the Annual Math Competition. (2) Wilbur Middle School would be sending five of its brightest students to compete against other area schools. (3) Students at Wilbur enjoy all their after-school clubs. (4) Tim was hoping that all of his studying would pay off in the contest. (5) After completing the written portion of the test, he exited with a confident look on his face. (6) Tim took the individual ribbon for third place and his team won a trophy for first place overall. (7) Tim and his team members waited anxiously as they began to announce the winners.

1 Which of the following is the most effective topic sentence for the paragraph?
   A Wilbur Middle School is located next to the city swimming pool.
   B Wilbur Middle School has 400 students enrolled.
   C Students at Wilbur Middle School participated in the math competition.
   D Wilbur Middle School has the highest standardized test scores in the state.

2 Which of the following sentences is most irrelevant and could be deleted from the paragraph?
   F The school would be sending five of its brightest students to compete against other area schools.
   G Students at Wilbur enjoy all their after-school clubs.
   H Tim was hoping that all of his studying would pay off in the contest.
   J Tim and his team members waited anxiously as they began to announce the winners.

3 Which of the following is the most logical sentence sequence for this paragraph?
   A 1, 3, 2, 4, 5, 6, 7
   B 7, 6, 2, 1, 3, 4, 5
   C 4, 1, 6, 7, 5, 3, 2
   D 1, 2, 3, 4, 5, 7, 6

4 If the writer wanted to add more information to this passage, which of the following would be most appropriate?
   F Tim was also a member of the art club.
   G Tim's mom gave him a ride to the math contest.
   H Tim was nervous as he entered the classroom.
   J Tim has one brother and one sister.

5 The tone of this passage can be described as—
   A happy
   B humorous
   C scary
   D bewildering

6 Which of the following sentences would best conclude the paragraph?
   F The high school is very close to Wilbur Middle School.
   G Tim always gets straight A's in math.
   H Tim broke the tip on his pencil during the test.
   J Tim's classmates were very proud of his achievement.

Analyzing Strategy, Organization, and Style

Directions: Read the passage, and then answer the questions that follow. Mark the letter of your answer on a bubble sheet if your teacher provides one; otherwise, number from 1 to 6 on a separate sheet of paper, and write the letter of the correct answer next to each number.

---

(1) Randy woke up before sunrise on Saturday. (2) She had to get her things together for the camping trip. (3) After arriving at the park, the troop's first task was to set up camp. (4) Randy's tent seemed to have a mind of its own, but she was finally able to assemble it with the help of the troop leader. (5) Randy's tent was red with a black rain guard. (6) The girls then went to the lake to try to catch their dinner. (7) While trying to reel the fish in, though, she lost her footing and slipped into the edge of the water! (8) After what seemed to be an eternity, Randy finally felt a tug on her line. (9) As she came back to dry land, Randy said: "It looks like the fish won this battle!"

---

1 Which of the following is the most effective topic sentence for the paragraph?
A Randy had never been camping before.
B Randy has a big backyard at her house.
C Randy is the first baseman for her baseball team.
D Randy was planning a trip to her grandparents' house.

2 Which of the following sentences could be switched to make this paragraph more logical?
F 5 and 6
G 6 and 7
H 7 and 8
J 8 and 9

3 Which of the following sentences could best be inserted between sentences 2 and 3?
A Randy has a brother named Willie.
B Randy's brother likes to go camping, too.
C Her troop was going to the state park to spend the weekend fishing and hiking.
D Randy likes to eat fish for dinner.

4 Which of the following sentences is most irrelevant and could be deleted from the paragraph?
F Randy's tent seemed to have a mind of its own, but she was finally able to assemble it with the help of the troop leader.
G Randy's tent was red with a black rain guard.
H After what seemed to be an eternity, Randy finally felt a tug on her line.
J While trying to reel the fish in, though, she lost his footing and slipped into the edge of the water!

5 The tone of this passage can be described as—
A serious
B humorous
C mysterious
D angry

6 Which of the following sentences would best conclude the paragraph?
F Randy wished she could go camping every weekend.
G Randy's mom bought her a brand-new tent for the trip.
H Randy likes to eat pizza for dinner.
J Randy then went back to camp to set up her tent.

Using Narration to Respond to Writing Prompts

Standardized tests often include a writing section in which you are asked to tell a story in order to express an opinion and argue for a course of action. Use these pages to plan and develop an essay in which you give and support an opinion.

Sample Writing Situation

> Your school is considering cutting back on field trips. Some think that the money spent on these trips would be better spent on books for the library or on computers that will provide Internet access.
>
> In an essay for the school newspaper, argue for or against eliminating school field trips in favor of buying more library books or computers for Internet access. To support your opinion, give your own experiences on field trips and with the school library and computers for research.

Who is the audience? _____

_____

What is the purpose of your response? _____

_____

What is the format of your response? _____

_____

What two tasks are identified? _____

_____

Prewriting

Complete the left column of the chart by listing experiences you have had on field trips. Complete the right column by jotting down some experiences you have had using the school library and/or computers.

Field Trip Experiences	School Library/ Computer Experiences

To take a stand on the issue, review your chart and circle the column that best represents your opinion.

Using Narration to Respond to Writing Prompts (continued)

Drafting

Do you favor funding field trips or the library and computers? Express your opinion in a sentence.

_____

_____

_____

_____

Write a paragraph that tells a story of your experiences with field trips.

_____

_____

_____

_____

_____

_____

Write a paragraph that tells a story of your experiences with the school library.

_____

_____

_____

_____

_____

_____

_____

On a separate sheet of paper, use your prewriting and drafting notes to draft your essay. Be sure to write an introduction, body, and conclusion.

Revising

As you revise your draft, ask what main point you make in your essay. Check to see if you have included any details that do not support your main point. Identify and explain two revisions you have made to your essay.

Revision 1: _____

_____

_____

Revision 2: _____

_____

_____

Responding to Writing Prompts About Narratives

Standardized tests often require you to respond to short stories you have read. Use these pages to plan and develop a response to the following prompt.

Sample Writing Situation

> Read "The Snow in Chelm" by Isaac Bashevis Singer on page 74 of *Prentice Hall Writing and Grammar: Communication in Action*, Copper Level. Then, answer the following question.
>
> What is the author's opinion of the way the Elders of Chelm make their decisions? Use details and information from the story in your answer.

Who is the audience for your response? _____

_____

What is the purpose of your response? _____

_____

What is the format of your response? _____

_____

Prewriting

Scan the story for specific information about the Elders' decisions. Write down two of these decisions and their results.

Decision: _____   Results: _____

Decision: _____   Results: _____

As you gather information, fill in the T-Chart below. In the left column, list the decisions the Elders make. In the right column, jot down the reasons they arrive at each decision.

The Elders' Decisions	Reasons

To analyze your chart, review each decision. Place a check next to those decisions that you think the author felt were good. Place an "X" next to those decisions the author probably thought were bad.

Responding to Writing Prompts About Narratives (continued)

Drafting

Write an introduction that clearly states what you will address in your response.

_____

_____

_____

_____

_____

_____

Write one main point from your essay and list details from the story that support that point.

_____

_____

_____

_____

_____

_____

_____

Now, write your full essay on a separate sheet of paper. Make sure to use specific examples from the story to support your main points.

Revising

Reread your essay focusing on the main points. To delete details that do not support the main idea, draw a line. To add examples for more support, use a caret. Identify and explain two revisions you've made to your work.

Revision 1: _____

_____

_____

Revision 2: _____

_____

_____

Analyzing Strategy, Organization, and Style

Directions: Read the passage, and then answer the questions that follow. Choose the letter of the best answer. Mark the letter of your answer on a bubble sheet if your teacher provides one; otherwise, number from 1 to 6 on a separate sheet of paper, and write the letter of the correct answer next to each number.

---

(1) Ranger Hanrahan told us that the Tate House was in fairly good shape. (2) Also that the grounds needed some serious work. (3) Over the past few years, he said, the gardens and the bushes had become completely overgrown. (4) Our people planned a bake sale to raise money to buy some plants and new tools to use at the house. (5) I wanted to make cranberry bran muffins for the sale, but Jon-Marc wanted to make orange oatmeal bread.

(6) In February, I decided that I really wanted to join the Young Conservationists (the YCs) with my friend Jon-Marc. (7) Last year, the YCs repaired a crumbling covered bridge on Comanche River. (8) The YCs help park rangers preserve historic sites in local, state, and national parks.

(9) The YCs had their first annual meeting in March. (10) Bill Hanrahan, a ranger from Hazel Park, gave a presentation on our project. (11) He told us that the YCs were going to work on the Tate House, a log cabin in the park. (12) Kirk and Ellen Tate, two immigrants, built the cabin in 1855. (13) When their daughter Kathleen was born a few years later, they planted a willow tree in her honor on the banks of Whitehead Creek.

---

1 In which part should the underlined word be replaced by a more precise word?
A Part 4
B Part 8
C Part 10
D Part 13

2 Which of the following is the best order for the paragraphs?
F 3, 2, 1
G 1, 3, 2
H 2, 3, 1
J Correct as is

3 Which of the following would be the best way to write parts 1 and 2?
A Ranger Hanrahan told us that the Tate House was in fairly good shape, but that the grounds needed some serious work.
B Ranger Hanrahan told us that the Tate House was in fairly good shape, or that the grounds needed some serious work.
C Ranger Hanrahan told us that the Tate House was in fairly good shape. In addition, that the grounds needed some serious work.
D The grounds needed some serious work, and Ranger Hanrahan told us that the Tate House was in fairly good shape.

4 Which of the following sentences could be inserted between parts 12 and 13?
F The city created the park in 1974.
G Ranger Hanrahan's parents came from Ireland.
H They moved to our area from Scotland.
J Last year, a bad storm hit the park and destroyed the playground area.

5 Choose the most logical sentence sequence for paragraph 2.
A 8, 6, 7
B 6, 8, 7
C 7, 8, 6
D Correct as is

6 In paragraph 1, which of the following should be deleted as irrelevant?
F Ranger Hanrahan told us that the Tate House was in fairly good shape.
G Over the past few years, he said, the gardens and the bushes had become completely overgrown.
H Our people planned a bake sale to raise money to buy some plants and new tools to use at the house.
J I wanted to make cranberry bran muffins for the sale, but Jon-Marc wanted to make orange oatmeal bread.

Analyzing Strategy, Organization, and Style

Directions: Read the passage, and then answer the questions that follow. Choose the letter of the best answer. Mark the letter of your answer on a bubble sheet if your teacher provides one; otherwise, number from 1 to 6 on a separate sheet of paper, and write the letter of the correct answer next to each number.

---

(1) We all get along really well, but sometimes it's hard to coordinate things with so many people. (2) On the weekend of the twenty-fourth, for example, my <u>sis</u> wanted to go to my basketball game, but my brother wanted to go to my cousin's soccer game. (3) My uncle wanted to go to the art museum party at night, and my aunt wanted to see a movie.

(4) My extended <u>family</u> does a lot of things together. (5) We had a busy weekend last month. (6) On Friday the twenty-fourth, we held a secret planning <u>meeting</u> for my grandfather's birthday party. (7) He's going to be ninety-four in June! (8) On Saturday the twenty-fifth, I played in a basketball game, and my cousin Maureen competed in a soccer game. (9) On Sunday the twenty-sixth, we staged our weekly barbecue. (10) We all love grilled chicken.

(11) My extended family lives on Sycamore Street. (12) Even my second cousins twice removed. (13) Between all of my different aunts and <u>uncles</u>, my family owns almost all the houses on the street! (14) Sycamore is a really nice street, with lots of trees.

---

1 In which part should the underlined word be replaced by a more formal word?
A Part 2
B Part 4
C Part 6
D Part 13

2 Which of the following is the best order for the paragraphs?
F 1, 3, 2
G 3, 2, 1
H 2, 1, 3
J Correct as is

3 Which of the following would be the best way to write parts 11 and 12?
A My extended family, and my second cousins twice removed, lives on Sycamore Street.
B My extended family lives on Sycamore Street. Along with my second cousins twice removed.
C My extended family lives on Sycamore Street. And my second cousins twice removed.
D My extended family—even my second cousins twice removed—lives on Sycamore Street.

4 Which of the following sentences could be inserted between parts 13 and 14?
F Most of the houses on Sycamore are bungalows.
G My uncle's name is Robert.
H Two of my cousins immigrated to the United States from Great Britain two years ago.
J My grandparents lived on Poplar Avenue when they first moved to town, but that was a long time ago.

5 Choose the most logical sentence sequence for paragraph 1.
A 3, 1, 2
B 1, 3, 2
C 2, 3, 1
D Correct as is

6 In paragraph 2, which of the following sentences should be deleted as irrelevant?
F We had a busy weekend last month.
G On Saturday the twenty-fifth, I played in a basketball game, and my cousin Maureen competed in a soccer game.
H On Sunday the twenty-sixth, we staged our weekly barbecue.
J We all love grilled chicken.

Responding to Persuasive Writing Prompts

Standardized tests often require you to write persuasively. Use these pages to plan and develop a response to the following prompt.

Sample Writing Situation

> The faculty and students at your school are being asked to vote on a logo for the school's Web page. The principal as well as many teachers believe that it should represent learning. They are considering an image of a book with the word *Sapientia*, the Latin word for *wisdom*, beneath it. Many students, on the other hand, want something more lively. They think the school mascot, a tiger, should be the logo. Choose one of the following prompts to which to respond.
>
> > State your position on the Web page logo in a letter to the editor of your school newspaper. Support your position with arguments, examples, and your own experiences.
>
> > State your position on the Web page logo in a letter to your school principal. Support your position with arguments, examples, and your own experiences.

Choose one prompt to address.

Who is the audience for your response? _____

_____

What is the purpose of your response? _____

_____

What is the format of your response? _____

_____

Prewriting

To gather support for your response, complete the T-Chart with logical arguments, facts, and examples on both sides of the issue.

Book Logo	Tiger Logo

Review your T-chart to decide which arguments will most persuade your audience. Circle each of your strongest arguments.

Write a sentence or two stating your position on what the Web page logo should be.

_____

_____

Responding to Persuasive Writing Prompts *(continued)*

Drafting

Write an introduction that clearly states your position. Make sure your introduction grabs your specific audience's attention.

_____

_____

_____

_____

_____

_____

Write down the details from your T-Chart that support your position. For each main idea, add supporting details.

Main idea: _____

   Details _____

_____

Main idea: _____

   Details _____

_____

Review your T-chart and choose one idea that supports the other side of the argument. State the idea and then write a few sentences to disprove it.

_____

_____

_____

_____

Now, use your prewriting and drafting notes to write your full essay on a separate sheet of paper.

Revising

Reread your essay to see if you have left out any important details. Identify one sentence and explain how you could change it to better support your position.

_____

_____

_____

Note places in your paper where you have used vague words. Identify two words to revise. Then, explain how replacing them with more precise words will strengthen your argument.

_____

_____

_____

Name _____ Date _____

Comparing and Contrasting in Response to Writing Prompts

Standardized tests often require you to produce an expository writing essay in which you compare and contrast people, items, or ideas. Use these pages to plan and develop a response to the following prompt.

Sample Writing Situation

> Read "More Than a Pinch: Two Salt Lakes" on page 152 *of Prentice Hall Writing and Grammar: Communication in Action*, Copper Level, and then answer the prompt below.
>
> In "More Than a Pinch: Two Salt Lakes," the writer compares the Great Salt Lake with the Dead Sea. Describe the ways the lakes are *alike* and *different*, using examples from the article.

Who is the audience? _____
_____

What is the purpose of your response? _____
_____

What is the format of your response? _____
_____

What tasks are identified? _____
_____

Prewriting

Write details from the essay in the Venn diagram below. Write similarities—characteristics common to both lakes—in the overlapping area. Write differences—characteristics unique to one lake—in the outer sections below the appropriate label.

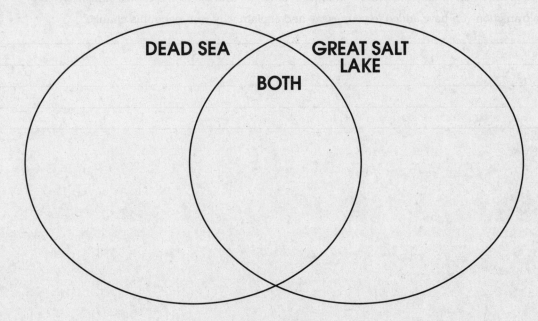

DEAD SEA   GREAT SALT LAKE

BOTH

Comparing and Contrasting in Response to Writing Prompts (*continued*)

Drafting

Identify the points of comparison you will address

_____

_____

_____

_____

_____

_____

For your introduction, write a general statement comparing the two lakes.

_____

_____

_____

_____

_____

Choose the organizational plan that best suits your prewriting work.

☐ Point-by-point: Discuss major points of comparison in turn.

☐ Subject-by-subject: Discuss one lake and all its points of comparison and then the other lake and all its points of comparison.

Now use your prewriting and drafting notes to write your essay on a separate sheet of paper.

Revising

Reread your essay to check the organization of ideas. Consider including transitions such as *but, however, yet,* and *in contrast,* to show difference and *in addition, similarly,* and *too* to emphasize similarity.

Identify one transition you have added to your essay and explain why you made this change.

_____

_____

_____

_____

Using Cause-and-Effect Writing for Expository Writing Prompts

Standardized tests often require you to produce an expository writing passage showing cause-and-effect relationships. Use these pages to plan and develop a response to the following prompt.

Sample Writing Situation

> West Indian manatees are not hunted by other animals, but they have come to be endangered. Read "Gentle Giants in Trouble" by Ross Bankson, in which he explains the causes of the manatee's problem. You can find the essay on page 176 *of Prentice Hall Writing and Grammar: Communication in Action*, Copper Level. Then, respond to the following prompt:
>
> > Explain three main causes for the endangerment of manatees. In your response, use details from Ross Bankson's article.

Who is the audience for your response? _____

_____

What is the purpose of your response? _____

_____

What is the format of your response? _____

_____

Prewriting

Read "Gentle Giants in Trouble" and start a cluster diagram by writing down each of three main causes for the endangerment of the manatees. Place each cause in a circle below.

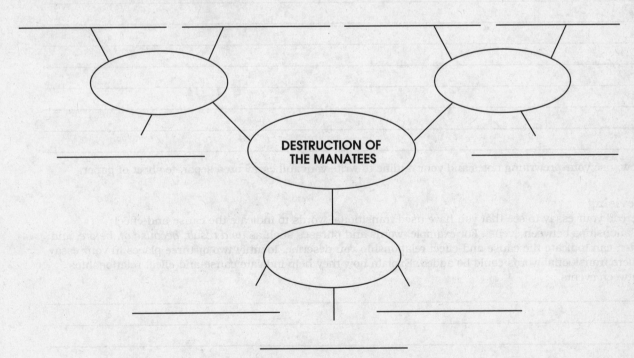

DESTRUCTION OF THE MANATEES

Finish the cluster diagram by completing the blanks by jotting down related events and situations for each cause.

Review the diagram and number all of the events associated with a main cause in order.

Using Cause-and-Effect Writing for Expository Writing Prompts (continued)

Drafting

Use the information in your cluster diagram to make an outline of your essay. For each letter, identify a main cause. Below each letter, jot down related events and details.

Title: Three Main Causes for the Endangerment of Manatees

A. _____

    1. _____

    2. _____

    3. _____

B. _____

    1. _____

    2. _____

    3. _____

C. _____

    1. _____

    2. _____

    3. _____

Write the paragraph that develops the ideas presented in the first section of your outline.

_____

_____

_____

_____

_____

_____

_____

Now, use your prewriting notes and your outline to write your full essay on a separate sheet of paper.

Revising

Reread your essay to see that you have used transitional words to indicate the cause-and-effect relationships between events. For example, words and phrases such as *as a result, because of, before,* and *after,* can indicate the cause-and-effect relationship you describe. Identify two or three places in your essay where transitional words could be added. Explain how they help indicate cause-and-effect relationships between events.

_____

_____

_____

_____

_____

_____

Responding to Expository Writing Prompts

Standardized tests often require you to produce an expository writing passage. Use these pages to plan and develop a response to the following prompt.

Sample Writing Situation

> Imagine that you have been asked to help a group of kindergartners learn how to tie their shoes.
>
> As the basis for the lesson you will give, write a how-to for beginners on tying one's shoes.

Who is the audience for your response? _____

_____

What is the purpose of your response? _____

_____

What is the format of your response? _____

_____

Prewriting

Think about who you will be instructing on tying a shoe. Write a sentence or two explaining how you can write something kindergartners will understand.

_____

_____

_____

Think about the steps involved in tying your shoes. Use the chart below to identify the steps in the order they must be completed.

How to tie a shoe . . .

Review your chart to determine whether you have included all of the steps. Add any that you may have taken for granted. For example, don't forget to tell readers to put their shoes on their feet.

Responding to Expository Writing Prompts *(continued)*

Drafting

Write an introduction sentence that grabs your audience's interest in your topic.

_____

_____

_____

_____

_____

Choose one step of the process and write a paragraph to show readers how to do it. Use language and details that your audience will understand.

_____

_____

_____

_____

_____

_____

_____

_____

_____

Now, use your prewriting and drafting notes to write your full essay on a separate sheet of paper. Make sure that each sentence describes only one step and that the steps are linked with transitional words.

Revising

Reread your essay to see if you can follow the instructions that you wrote. Rewrite any sections that were confusing to follow. Identify two changes you made. For each, explain your reasons for the changes you made.

Revision 1: _____

_____

_____

Revision 2: _____

_____

Revising and Editing

Directions: Read the following passage. Then answer the questions below, choosing the letter of the best answer. Mark the letter of your answer on a bubble sheet if your teacher provides one; otherwise, number from 1 to 6 on a separate sheet of paper, and write the letter of the correct answer next to each number.

---

1 Gray wolves once lived in every part of the Northern Hemisphere except tropical
2 forests and arid deserts. However, they have disappearing in many of these places and
3 their numbers are decreasing in other areas. They formerly lived in all parts of North
4 America, but now they like to live in Canada and Alaska, and in smaller numbers in
5 Minnesota and Mexico. An effort also began in 1995 to reintroduce the gray wolf in parts
6 of the northern Rocky Mountains.
7 The gray wolf is a powerful animal with dense, long, and soft fur. It is an intelligent,
8 social animal that usually lives in packs. This wolf feeds primarily on large animals such
9 as deer or moose. However, it may also attack domestic livestock, which has made it
10 unpopular with some humans who don't like that. Contrary to what many believe, there
11 have been few, if any, wolf attacks on humans in North America.

---

1 What is the **BEST** change, if any, to make to the sentence in lines 2–3 (*"However . . . areas."*)?
   A Change *decreasing* to **decreased**
   B Change *disappearing* to **disappear**
   C Change *disappearing* to **disappeared**
   D Make no change.

2 What is the **BEST** change, if any, to make in the middle of the sentence in lines 3–4 (*"It . . . Mexico."*)?
   F Change *they like to live* to **it is going to live**
   G Change *like to live* to **are going to live**
   H Change *like to live* to **primarily live**
   J Make no change.

3 Which of the following sentences would **BEST** fit after the sentence in lines 4–6 (*"An . . . Mountains."*)?
   A Hopefully, efforts such as this will help to restore the wolf population.
   B The Rocky Mountains are really beautiful.
   C Wolves seem to like living in the mountains.
   D At that time, Bill Clinton was President of the United States in 1995.

4 Which of these sentences would **BEST** fit the ideas in lines 8–9 (*"This . . . moose."*)?
   F There are a lot of moose in Canada.
   G These animals are found in the wild.
   H Deer and moose are both big animals.
   J Deer meat is also called venison.

5 Which is the **BEST** change, if any, that should be made to the sentence in lines 9–10 (*"However . . . that."*)?
   A Delete *who don't like that*
   B Change *humans who don't like that* to **humans like that**
   C Change *humans who don't like that* to **unlikable humans**
   D Make no change.

6 Which of the following sentences would **BEST** conclude the passage?
   F Wolves should be able to live wherever they want!
   G The gray wolf and humans must work together to ensure the survival of each.
   H Humans should respect the gray wolf and attempt to preserve its species.
   J Most humans will never see a gray wolf.

Revising and Editing

Directions: Read the following passage. Then answer the questions below, choosing the letter of the best answer. Mark the letter of your answer on a bubble sheet if your teacher provides one; otherwise, number from 1 to 6 on a separate sheet of paper, and write the letter of the correct answer next to each number.

> 1   Dolphins have produced a wide variety of squeals, squeaks, and other sounds,
> 2   which they use to communicate and navigate. Many scientists have studied the sounds
> 3   dolphins make. These scientists have figured out that all dolphins have a signature
> 4   whistle. Dolphins are given his signature whistle, which is like a name, at birth.
> 5   Dolphins also use sounds in a process known as echolocation. The dolphin sends
> 6   out an echo and it is received after bouncing off an object. From this echo the dolphin can
> 7   tell things such as the size and shape of the object. Dolphins can use this technique to
> 8   find things like food and each other. They can also use it to find their way around if the
> 9   water is dark or murky.

1 What is the **BEST** change, if any, to make to the sentence in lines 1–2 *("Dolphins . . . navigate.")*?
A Change *Dolphins* to **They**
B Change *have produced* to **produce**
C Change *have produced* to **have been producing**
D Make no change.

2 Which of the following sentences would **BEST** fit after the sentence in lines 2–3 *("Many . . . make.")*?
F Some of them think that dolphins have their own language.
G Almost all animals make some type of sound.
H Dolphins have also studied these sounds.
J The ocean has many different sounds.

3 What is the **BEST** change, if any, to make to the sentence in line 4 *("Dolphins . . . birth.")*?
A Change *his* to **its**
B Change *his* to **his or her**
C Change *his* to **their**
D Make no change.

4 Which of these sentences would **BEST** fit the ideas in line 5 *("Dolphins . . . echolocation.")*?

F There are many sounds that the dolphin uses.
G A process is a series of actions that leads to an end.
H Echolocation is the ability to use sound to "see" things.
J A dolphin is a type of whale.

5 Which is the **BEST** change, if any, that should be made to the sentence in lines 6–7 *("From . . . object.")*?
A Change *can tell* to **can be telling**
B Change *can tell* to **told**
C Change *such as the size* to **such as to the size**
D Make no change.

6 Which of the following sentences would **BEST** conclude the passage?
F Dolphins produce both high and low frequency sounds.
G Some of the sounds that dolphins make cannot be heard by humans.
H Dolphins use sound in many ways to make their lives easier.
J Dolphins don't have vocal cords in their throat like humans do.

Responding to Prompts About Literature

Standardized tests often require you to respond to a literary work or passage. Use these pages to plan and develop a response to the following prompt.

Sample Writing Situation

Read the following poem by Theodore Roethke.

"Child on Top of a Greenhouse."

(1) The wind bellowing out the seat of my britches,
(2) My feet crackling splinters of glass and dried putty,
(3) The half-grown chrysanthemums staring up like accusers,
(4) Up through the streaked glass, flashing with sunlight,
(5) A few white clouds all rushing eastward,
(6) A line of elms plunging and tossing like horses,
(7) And everyone, everyone pointing and shouting!

"Child on Top of a Greenhouse" is a good example of the use of perspective, or point of view, in poetry. Write an essay in which you explain the point of view of the speaker in the poem. Answer these questions: Where is the speaker? What can the speaker see from this perspective? Then, explain how the poet uses details to help the reader share in this perspective.

Who is the audience for your response? _____

What is the purpose of your response? _____

What is the format of your response? _____

Prewriting

Complete the graphic organizer below. In the inner circles, list details about the speaker. On the lines, list examples from the poem that support each detail.

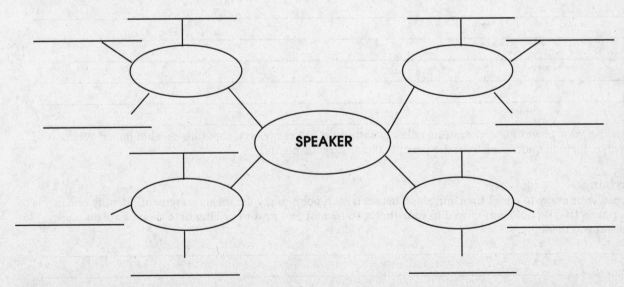

Write a sentence stating where the speaker is and how this affects what he can see. This is your thesis statement.

_____

_____

_____

Which examples from the poem most strongly support your thesis? Review your organizer and place a check in the circles containing your strongest examples. Use these as the support for your response.

Responding to Prompts About Literature *(continued)*

Drafting

Write an opening paragraph starting with your thesis statement. Then complete the introduction by identifying the details you will discuss.

_____

_____

_____

_____

_____

_____

Choose one word or phrase and write a sentence or two to explain how the poet uses special language to convey what it feels like to see the world from that perspective.

_____

_____

_____

_____

Write a body paragraph to discuss one of the examples from your graphic organizer. Explain how each image shows something the speaker could see only from his point of view.

_____

_____

_____

_____

_____

_____

_____

_____

Now, use your prewriting and drafting notes to write your full essay on a separate sheet of paper. When possible, include quotations from the poem to illustrate your points.

Revising

Reread your essay to check the connection between each point and your thesis statement. Identify one or two points that do not connect well to your thesis statement and reword or eliminate them. Explain one revision you made.

_____

_____

_____

_____

_____

_____

_____

Proofreading

Directions: Read the following passage and decide which type of errors, if any, appear in the underlined sections. Choose the letter of the best answer. Mark the letter of your answer on a bubble sheet if your teacher provides one; otherwise, number from 1 to 6 on a separate sheet of paper, and write the letter of the correct answer next to each number.

Álvar Núñez Cabeza de Vaca was an important spanish explorer. In 1528 Cabeza de Vaca and
                                              (1)

other explorers were shipwrecked off the coast of present-day Texas. Cabeza de Vaca and three

other men survived a wide varyity of dangers, including illnesses and injuries. Mariame Indians
                          (2)

later enslaved the Spaniards making them decide to escape. Cabeza de Vaca and the others
                    (3)

succeeded and headed toward Mexico. They eventualy reached Culiacán in 1536. An article in
                            (4)   (5)

the magazine Southwestern Historical Quarterly provides interesting information about Cabeza
             (6)

de Vaca's route across Texas.

---

1 **A** Spelling error
　　B Capitalization error
　　C Punctuation error
　　D No error

2 **F** Spelling error
　　G Capitalization error
　　H Punctuation error
　　J No error

3 **A** Spelling error
　　B Capitalization error
　　C Punctuation error
　　D No error

4 **F** Spelling error
　　G Capitalization error
　　H Punctuation error
　　J No error

5 **A** Spelling error
　　B Capitalization error
　　C Punctuation error
　　D No error

6 **F** Spelling error
　　G Capitalization error
　　H Punctuation error
　　J No error

Proofreading

Directions: Read the following passage and decide which type of errors, if any, appear in the underlined sections. Choose the letter of the best answer. Mark the letter of your answer on a bubble sheet if your teacher provides one; otherwise, number from 1 to 6 on a separate sheet of paper, and write the letter of the correct answer next to each number.

Jim was a little <u>nervus</u> when <u>our Principal</u> gave our class an assignment on
(1)   (2)

<u>spanish</u> explorers. Last month, we wrote term papers on the French explorers, and Jim <u>didnt</u>
(3)   (4)

do very well. There were a lot of French explorers who led expeditions in the United States

during the 1600's and 1700's. Jim had a hard time keeping them <u>seperate</u>. The University of
(5)

Texas Press just published a book called <u>"Spanish Explorers in Present-Day Texas."</u> Jim hopes
(6)

that the book will help him on the new assignment.

---

1 **A** Spelling error
    B Capitalization error
    C Punctuation error
    D No error

2 **F** Spelling error
    G Capitalization error
    H Punctuation error
    J No error

3 **A** Spelling error
    B Capitalization error
    C Punctuation error
    D No error

4 **F** Spelling error
    G Capitalization error
    H Punctuation error
    J No error

5 **A** Spelling error
    B Capitalization error
    C Punctuation error
    D No error

6 **F** Spelling error
    G Capitalization error
    H Punctuation error
    J No error

Completing Analogies

Directions: Each question below consists of a related pair of words or phrases, followed by five pairs of words or phrases labeled A through E. Select the pair that best expresses a relationship similar to that expressed in the original pair. Choose the letter of the best answer. Mark the letter of your answer on a bubble sheet if your teacher provides one; otherwise, number from 1 to 6 on a separate sheet of paper, and write the letter of the correct answer next to each number.

1 BITTER : SWEET ::
  A tart : sour
  B smiling : expression
  C spice : salty
  D clustered : spilled
  E clumsy : graceful

2 SUFFER : COMPLAINING ::
  A war : clash
  B thicken : dilute
  C sip : thirst
  D enjoy : enthusiasm
  E soothe : stroke

3 TELEGRAPH : COMMUNICATE ::
  A train : travel
  B fame : superstar
  C briefcase : achieve
  D write : journal
  E cafeteria : eat

4 BALMY : WEATHER ::
  A force : trickle
  B talented : flower
  C value : yoke
  D ignore : avoid
  E complicated : puzzle

5 PARKA : COAT ::
  A Siamese : dog
  B ice : rink
  C skirt : dress
  D palomino : horse
  E shoe : high heel

6 PERPLEX : CONFUSE ::
  A tinker : sketch
  B multiply : divide
  C shield : protect
  D witness : undertake
  E show : realize

Completing Analogies

Directions: Complete each item by choosing the phrase that best completes the sentence. Choose the letter of the best answer. Mark the letter of your answer on a bubble sheet if your teacher provides one; otherwise, number from 1 to 6 on a separate sheet of paper, and write the letter of the correct answer next to each number.

1 Candidate is to election as—
A jockey is to corral.
B dentist is to office.
C cowboy is to range.
D artist is to vacuum.
E player is to game.

2 Violin is to orchestra as—
A newspaper is to sports.
B bat is to puck.
C director is to choir.
D clarinet is to band.
E string is to woodwind.

3 Hickory is to tree as—
A senator is to representative.
B pine is to oak.
C igloo is to townhouse.
D pediatrician is to doctor.
E fastener is to bolt.

4 Sprain is to break as—
A ice is to heat.
B scream is to laugh.
C doubt is to wonder.
D spy is to glimpse.
E tap is to hammer.

5 Earth is to universe as—
A town is to city.
B Alabama is to United States.
C California is to Michigan.
D Great Britain is to United States.
E Los Angeles is to New York City.

6 Sincere is to phony as—
A angry is to furious.
B truthful is to honest.
C mammoth is to large.
D nimble is to slow.
E magnificent is to wonderful.

Standard English Usage: Verbs

Directions: Read the passage, and choose the letter of the word or group of words that belongs in each space. Mark the letter of your answer on a bubble sheet if your teacher provides one; otherwise, number from 1 to 6 on a separate sheet of paper, and write the letter of the correct answer next to each number.

Two years ago, Deborah and Kirk _____(1)_____ a dog wandering on a country road in Bastrop County. The dog _____(2)_____ thin and scratched. They wondered if he _____(3)_____ abandoned or _____(4)_____ escaped from a bad home. Deborah and Kirk _____(5)_____ the dog into their truck and drove him to their veterinarian, Dr. Megan DeMoss. Dr. DeMoss _____(6)_____ the dog for heartworm and surface cuts. Deborah and Kirk decided to adopt the dog and named him Hugger.

---

1   **A** did find
     B had found
     C finded
     D found

2   **F** were
     G was
     H be
     J is

3   **A** had been
     B likely was
     C would be
     D was been

4   **F** had been
     G was
     H would be
     J had

5   **A** loading
     B will load
     C did load
     D loaded

6   **F** will be treating
     G treats
     H treated
     J would treat

Standard English Usage: Verbs

Directions: Read the passage, and choose the letter of the word or group of words that belongs in each space. Mark the letter of your answer on a bubble sheet if your teacher provides one; otherwise, number from 1 to 6 on a separate sheet of paper, and write the letter of the correct answer next to each number.

Deborah and Kirk's new dog _____(1)_____ a labrador retriever. They _____(2)_____ that the dog was a labrador retriever when they first saw the animal on a country road in Bastrop County. Dr. Megan DeMoss, their veterinarian, soon _____(3)_____ their belief. Dr. DeMoss _____(4)_____ Deborah and Kirk some interesting information about labrador retrievers. She said that labrador retrievers _____(5)_____ the most popular breed of dog in the United States. In 1999, there were more than 154,000 labrador retrievers _____(6)_____ with the American Kennel Club.

---

1 A be
   B were
   C is
   D was

2 F had suspected
   G suspect
   H be suspecting
   J suspects

3 A confirm
   B had confirm
   C will confirm
   D confirmed

4 F had tell
   G be telling
   H told
   J tell

5 A are
   B is
   C was
   D be

6 F register
   G registering
   H registers
   J registered

Using Adjectives and Adverbs

Directions: Read the passage, and choose the letter of the word that belongs in each space. Mark the letter of your answer on a bubble sheet if your teacher provides one; otherwise, number from 1 to 6 on a separate sheet of paper, and write the letter of the correct answer next to each number.

Nearly every Sunday my family and I go riding on the hike and bike trail along the lake. There are so many things to see there. My sister always wants to stop and watch the canoes go ___(1)___ through the water. My brother enjoys focusing on the runners coming across the bridge to see which are the ___(2)___ . My dad prefers to find a ___(3)___ spot along the way and ___(4)___ watch the people go by. My mom, on the other hand, is more ___(5)___ . She always wants to be part of the action. Just last week, she joined a pick-up game of touch football. She shouted ___(6)___ after scoring a touchdown!

---

1 A graceful
   B gracefully
   C slow
   D smooth

2 F quickly
   G quicker
   H fastest
   J faster

3 A comfortable
   B conveniently
   C fairly
   D well

4 F frequent
   G frequented
   H simpler
   J simply

5 A loudly
   B excitedly
   C adventurous
   D adventure

6 F joyful
   G delightful
   H gleefully
   J excited

Using Adjectives and Adverbs

Directions: Read the passage. Some sections are underlined. Choose the best way to write each underlined section. Mark the letter of your answer on a bubble sheet if your teacher provides one; otherwise, number from 1 to 6 on a separate sheet of paper, and write the letter of the correct answer next to each number.

Our teacher gave us an assignment. The assignment was difficult. We had to research our
(1)

family history. I went to the library to begin the assignment. I went to the public library. There,
(2)   (3)

I was able to find some information. The information was beneficial. I decided it would be a good

idea to continue my search, though, and decided to interview my grandpa. He told many stories
(4)

about our family. The stories were interesting. He spoke of how my family arrived here and
(5)

began a new life. He spoke of this proudly. He showed me some photos. He finally showed me
(6)

some photos from his album. I feel fortunate to have learned more about my family's history.

---

1 **A** Our teacher gave us an assignment difficultly.
   B Our teacher gave us a difficult assignment.
   C Our difficult teacher gave us an assignment.
   D Our teacher difficultly gave us an assignment.

2 **F** I went to the public library to begin the assignment.
   G I publicly went to the library to begin the assignment.
   H I went to the library to begin the public assignment.
   J I went to the library to begin the assignment publicly.

3 **A** There, I was beneficially able to find some information.
   B Beneficially, I was able to find some information there.
   C There, I was able to beneficially find some information.
   D There, I was able to find some beneficial information.

4 **F** He interestingly told many stories about our family.
   G He told many stories about our interesting family.
   H Interestingly, he told many stories about our family.
   J He told many interesting stories about our family.

5 **A** He spoke of how my family arrived here and began a proud, new life.
   B He spoke proudly of how my family arrived here and began a new life.
   C He spoke of how my proud family arrived here and began a new life.
   D He spoke of how my family arrived here proudly and began a new life.

6 **F** Finally, he showed me some photos from his album.
   G He showed me some final photos from his album.
   H He showed me some photos from his final album.
   J He finally showed me some final photos from his album.

Revising and Editing

Directions: Read the passage, and choose the letter of the best way to write the underlined sentences. Mark the letter of your answer on a bubble sheet if your teacher provides one; otherwise, number from 1 to 4 on a separate sheet of paper, and write the letter of the correct answer next to each number.

<u>Bats are flying mammals that hang. Bats use their feet to hang.</u> <u>By day, bats roost. Trees,
(1)   (2)
caves, bridges, and the eaves of buildings are some places where bats roost.</u> Most kinds of bats

are helpful to people. <u>Fruit-eating bats pollinate bananas. They pollinate mango, cashew, and fig
                                     (3)
trees, too.</u> <u>Mexican free-tailed bats eat many insects every night. Otherwise there would be more
                       (4)
mosquitoes and pests.</u>

---

1 **A** Bats are flying mammals that hang; they use their feet.
  B When bats fly, they use their feet.
  C Bats can fly or hang using their feet.
  D Bats are flying mammals that hang by their feet.

2 **F** By day, bats roost in trees, caves, bridges, and the eaves of buildings.
  G By day, bats roost, for example in trees, caves, bridges, and the eaves of buildings.
  H By day, bats roost such as trees, caves, bridges, and the eaves of buildings.
  J By day, bats roost; some places where bats roost are trees, caves, bridges, and the eaves of buildings.

3 **A** Fruit-eating bats pollinate banana trees including mango, cashew, and fig trees.
  B Fruit-eating bats pollinate many types of trees inlcuding bananas, mangos, cashews, and figs.
  C Fruit-eating bats pollinate banana trees; they also pollinate mango, cashew, and fig trees, too.
  D Fruit-eating bats pollinate too many trees including banana trees, mangos, cashews, and figs.

4 **F** Mexican free-tailed bats eat mosquitoes and pests.
  G If not for Mexican free-tailed bats eating many insects every night, there would be more mosquitoes and pests.
  H Mexican free-tailed bats eat many insects every night. Without these bats, there would be more mosquitoes and pests.
  J Mexican free-tails eat many insects. Without these pests, there would be more mosquitoes.

Revising and Editing

Directions: Read the passage, and choose the letter of the best way to write the underlined sentences. Mark the letter of your answer on a bubble sheet if your teacher provides one; otherwise, number from 1 to 6 on a separate sheet of paper, and write the letter of the correct answer next to each number.

There are many different varieties of bats. <u>Some very small African bats live upon large spider</u>
(1)
<u>webs.</u> <u>Other bats have sticky patches that they use to hold into things.</u> <u>On the country of</u>
(2)   (3)
<u>Indonesia, some bats, called flying foxes, have wingspans as broad as six feet.</u> <u>Several types of</u>
(4)
<u>bats use leaves for shelter. They also use caves for shelter</u> <u>Some people do not like bats and</u>
(5)
<u>other people are afraid of bats.</u> <u>Now you can tell your friends some new facts you learned of</u>
(6)
<u>bats!</u>

1 A Some very small African bats live toward large spider webs.
B Some very small African bats live in large spider webs.
C Some very small African bats live within large spider webs.
D Some very small African bats live by large spider webs.

2 F Other bats have sticky patches that they use to hold onto things.
G Other bats have sticky patches that they use to hold between things.
H Other bats have sticky patches that they use to hold upon things.
J Other bats have sticky patches that they use to hold off things.

3 A At the country of Indonesia, some bats, called flying foxes, have wingspans as broad as six feet.
B By the country of Indonesia, some bats, called flying foxes, have wingspans as broad as six feet.
C In the country of Indonesia, some bats, called flying foxes, have wingspans as broad as six feet.
D From the country of Indonesia, some bats, called flying foxes, have wingspans as broad as six feet.

4 F Several types of bats use leaves for shelter, and caves.
G Several types of bats use leaves—and caves—for shelter.
H Several types of bats use leaves for shelter with caves.
J Several types of bats use leaves and caves for shelter.

5 A Some people do not like bats, and others are afraid of them.
B Some people do not like bats and are afraid of bats.
C Some people do not like bats but are afraid of them.
D Some people do not like bats in contrast, they are afraid of them.

6 F Now you can tell your friends some new facts you learned by bats!
G Now you can tell your friends some new facts you learned around bats!
H Now you can tell your friends some new facts you learned about bats!
J Now you can tell your friends some new facts you learned over bats!

Revising and Editing

Directions: Read the passage, and choose the letter of the best way to write the underlined sentences. If the underlined section needs no change, mark the choice "Correct as is." Mark the letter of your answer on a bubble sheet if your teacher provides one; otherwise, number from 1 to 6 on a separate sheet of paper, and write the letter of the correct answer next to each number.

At the beginning of the school year, the sixth grade music instructor invited all the students to

Instrument Night. He wanted them to look at all the different instruments. He wanted them to
                  (1)

pick an instrument for the year. Eli tried three different instruments. He liked the trumpet the
                                  (2)

best. His uncle had played the trumpet in sixth grade. That was probably the reason that Eli
     (3)

liked it the best. Kathleen picked the clarinet because her brother had an old one to give her.
                   (4)

The sixth grade music teacher told Eli and Kathleen that the trumpet and the clarinet had
(5)

complementary sounds. Also that they were important jazz instruments. Eli and Kathleen both
                                                                        (6)

liked jazz. They decided to form a small jazz practice group.

---

1 A He wanted them to look at all the different instruments. But he wanted them to pick an instrument for the year.
   B He wanted them to look at all the different instruments, because they could pick an instrument for the year.
   C He wanted them to look at all the different instruments, and to pick one for the year.
   D Correct as is

2 F Eli tried three different instruments, but he liked the trumpet the best.
   G Eli tried three different instruments. And he liked the trumpet the best.
   H Eli tried three different instruments, for he liked the trumpet the best.
   J Correct as is

3 A His uncle had played the trumpet in sixth grade, for that was probably the reason that Eli liked it the best.
   B His uncle had played the trumpet in sixth grade, and that was probably the reason that Eli liked it the best.
   C His uncle had played the trumpet in sixth grade, but that was probably the reason that Eli liked it the best.
   D Correct as is

4 F Kathleen picked the clarinet, her brother had an old one to give her.

G Kathleen picked the clarinet, and her brother had an old one to give her.
   H Kathleen picked the clarinet. Because her brother had an old one to give her.
   J Correct as is

5 A The sixth grade music teacher told Eli and Kathleen that the trumpet and the clarinet had complementary sounds. For they were important jazz instruments.
   B The sixth grade music teacher told Eli and Kathleen that the trumpet and the clarinet had complementary sounds, and that they were important jazz instruments.
   C The sixth grade music teacher told Eli and Kathleen that the trumpet and the clarinet had complementary sounds, because they were important jazz instruments.
   D Correct as is

6 F Eli and Kathleen both liked jazz, so they decided to form a small jazz practice group.
   G Eli and Kathleen both liked jazz, but they decided to form a small jazz practice group.
   H Eli and Kathleen both liked jazz. And they decided to form a small jazz practice group.
   J Correct as is

Revising and Editing

Directions: Read the passage, and choose the letter of the best way to write the underlined sentences. If the underlined section needs no change, mark the choice "Correct as is." Mark the letter of your answer on a bubble sheet if your teacher provides one; otherwise, number from 1 to 6 on a separate sheet of paper, and write the letter of the correct answer next to each number.

Eli thought that the band concert was on Thursday. Kathleen told him that it was on Friday.
(1)

She asked him to wear black pants and a white shirt. The players all wanted to look exactly the
(2)

same. Eli didn't have a white shirt, but he said that he would buy one. Kathleen suggested that
(3)   (4)

he could borrow one from Marc. Or from Jon. Eli said that his sleeve size was closer to Jon's,
(5)

and that his neck size was closer to Marc's. Eli decided to ask Marc to borrow his shirt, and he
(6)

and Kathleen went to rehearsal.

---

1 **A** Eli thought that the band concert was on Thursday, and Kathleen told him that it was on Friday.
  B Eli thought that the band concert was on Thursday, but Kathleen told him that it was on Friday.
  C Eli thought that the band concert was on Thursday, for Kathleen told him that it was on Friday.
  D Correct as is

2 **F** She asked him to wear black pants and a white shirt. For the players all wanted to look exactly the same.
  G She asked him to wear black pants and a white shirt and the players all wanted to look exactly the same.
  H She asked him to wear black pants and a white shirt, because the players all wanted to look exactly the same.
  J Correct as is

3 **A** Eli didn't have a white shirt, for he said that he would buy one.
  B Eli didn't have a white shirt. And he said that he would buy one.
  C Eli didn't have a white shirt. Even so, he said that he would buy one.
  D Correct as is

4 **F** Kathleen suggested that he could borrow one from Marc, and from Jon.
  G Kathleen suggested that he could borrow one from Marc, but from Jon.
  H Kathleen suggested that he could borrow one from Marc, or from Jon.
  J Correct as is

5 **A** Eli said that his sleeve size was closer to Jon's, or that his neck size was closer to Marc's.
  B Eli said that his sleeve size was closer to Jon's, but that his neck size was closer to Marc's.
  C Eli said that his sleeve size was closer to Jon's, because his neck size was closer to Marc's.
  D Correct as is

6 **F** Eli decided to ask Marc to borrow his shirt, but he and Kathleen went to rehearsal.
  G Eli decided to ask Marc to borrow his shirt. And he and Kathleen went to rehearsal.
  H Eli decided to ask Marc to borrow his shirt, because he and Kathleen went to rehearsal.
  J Correct as is

Recognizing Appropriate Sentence Construction

Directions: Read the passage, and choose the letter of the best way to write each underlined section. If the underlined section needs no change, choose "Correct as is." Mark the letter of your answer on a bubble sheet if your teacher provides one; otherwise, number from 1 to 4 on a separate sheet of paper, and write the letter of the correct answer next to each number.

For many years, people thought that Vikings might have reached North America before

Columbus, but there was no proof. In 1837, a Danish professor named Carl Christian Rafn:
                                     (1)

evidence that the Vikings discovered America. Claimed that Vinland, a place mentioned in two
                                               (2)

thirteenth-century Viking sagas, was actually North America. (Sagas are long tales of adventures

and heroes.) Many people read Rafn's book, interested in his theory. In 1960, Anne Stine and
               (3)

Helge Ingstad found the ruins of a Viking settlement in Newfoundland, Canada. Their discovery
                                                                                (4)

finally proved that Vikings settled North America 500 years before Columbus.

---

1 A In 1837, a Danish professor named Carl Christian Rafn found evidence that the Vikings discovered America.

B In 1837, a Danish professor—Carl Christian Rafn—evidence that the Vikings discovered America.

C In 1837, a Danish professor named Carl Christian Rafn. This is evidence that the Vikings discovered America.

D Correct as is

2 F Rafn claimed that Vinland. A place mentioned in two thirteenth-century Viking sagas was actually North America.

G A place mentioned in two thirteenth-century Viking sagas, claimed that Vinland, was actually North America.

H Rafn claimed that Vinland, a place mentioned in two thirteenth-century Viking sagas, was actually North America.

J Correct as is

3 A Many people read Rafn's book and became interested in his theory.

B Many people read Rafn's book. Interested in his theory.

C Many people read Rafn's book, became interested in his theory.

D Correct as is

4 F Their discovery! Finally proved that Vikings settled North America 500 years before Columbus.

G Their discovery finally, that Vikings settled North America 500 years before Columbus.

H Their finally proved that Vikings settled North America 500 years before Columbus.

J Correct as is

Recognizing Appropriate Sentence Construction

Directions: Read the passage, and choose the letter of the best way to write the underlined sentences. If the underlined section needs no change, choose "Correct as is." Mark the letter of your answer on a bubble sheet if your teacher provides one; otherwise, number from 1 to 6 on a separate sheet of paper, and write the letter of the correct answer next to each number.

Curling is a sport played on ice with a large, heavy granite stone. There are four players on each
(1)   (2)
curling team. Take turns running with a stone and shooting it across the ice. As one player
                                                                                                              (3)
shoots, two others sweep on the ice ahead of the stone with brooms. Sweeping smoothes and
                                                                                                    (4)
warms the ice, which makes the stone glide farther. The game is scored after all players have

shot two stones. In order to score, a stone must be closer to the tee, or center target. Than any
               (5)
of the opposing team's stones. Has been an Olympic medal sport since the 1998 Games in
                                       (6)
Japan.

1 A Curling is a sport some played on ice with a large, heavy granite stone.
   B If played on ice, curling is a sport with a large, heavy granite stone.
   C Curling is a sport. They played it on ice with a large, heavy granite stone.
   D Correct as is

2 F There are four players on each curling team, running with a stone and shooting it across the ice.
   G There are four players on each curling team. Players take turns running with a stone and shooting it across the ice.
   H There are four players on each curling team taking turns running with a stone and shooting it across the ice.
   J Correct as is

3 A As one player shoots, two others sweep the ice ahead of the stone with brooms.
   B As one player shoots. Two others are sweeping on the ice ahead of the stone with brooms.
   C As one player shoots, on the ice ahead of the stone sweeping with brooms are two others.
   D Correct as is

4 F They are sweeping smoothes and warms the ice, which it makes the stone glide farther.
   G By sweeping smoothes and warms the ice, then makes the stone glide farther.
   H Sweeping smoothes and warms the ice. He makes the stone glide farther.
   J Correct as is

5 A In order to score, a stone is closer to the tee, or center target, than any of the opposing team's stones.
   B A stone that must be closer to the tee, or center target, than any of the opposing team's stones scores.
   C In order to score, a stone must be closer to the tee, or center target, than any of the opposing team's stones.
   D Correct as is

6 F Has been an Olympic medal sport. Since the 1998 Games in Japan.
   G Curling has been an Olympic medal sport since the 1998 Games in Japan.
   H It has been an Olympic medal sport since the 1998 Games in Japan.
   J Correct as is

Revising and Editing

Directions: Choose the letter of the best way to write each underlined section. If the underlined section needs no change, choose "Correct as is." Mark the letter of your answer on a bubble sheet if your teacher provides one; otherwise, number from 1 to 6 on a separate sheet of paper, and write the letter of the correct answer next to each number.

Carlsbad Caverns is a national park. It is located in southeastern New Mexico. Under the park
(1)   (2)
is a collection of underground chambers. The park is seventy-three square miles in area.

Carlsbad Caverns has a deep limestone cave. It is 1,597 feet deep. There are nearly 1 million
(3)   (4)
bats that live in Carlsbad Caverns during part of the year. They are Mexican Freetail bats.

During the day they crowd together on the cavern's ceilings. And at nightfall leave the cave in
(5)
giant swarms. Carlsbad Caverns is a spectacular sight. Everyone should see it.
              (6)

---

1 A Carlsbad Caverns is a national park and southeastern New Mexico is where it is.
B In New Mexico, Carlsbad Caverns, in the southeast, is a national park.
C Carlsbad Caverns is a national park located in southeastern New Mexico.
D Correct as is

2 F Seventy-three square miles under the park is a collection of underground chambers.
G Under the park, which is seventy-three square miles in area, is a collection of underground chambers.
H Under the park, which is square, is a collection of seventy-three underground chambers.
J Correct as is

3 A Carlsbad Caverns has a limestone cave which is 1,597 feet deep.
B Carlsbad Caverns has a really deep limestone cave, 1,597 feet deep.
C Carlsbad Caverns is 1,597 feet deep and has a limestone cave.
D Correct as is

4 F There are nearly one million Mexican Freetail bats that live in Carlsbad Caverns during part of the year.

G Nearly one million bats, Mexican Freetail bats, live in Carlsbad Caverns during part of the year.
H During part of the year in Carlsbad Caverns live Mexican Freetail bats, nearly one million.
J Correct as is

5 A During the day and at nightfall they form together on the cavern's ceilings in giant swarms.
B During the day they crowd together on the cavern's ceilings so they can leave the cave in giant swarms at nightfall.
C During the day they crowd together on the cavern's ceilings; at nightfall they leave the cave in giant swarms.
D Correct as is

6 F Carlsbad Caverns is a spectacular sight because everyone should see it.
G Everyone should see Carlsbad Caverns that is a spectacular sight.
H Carlsbad Caverns, seen by everyone, is a spectacular sight.
J Correct as is

Revising and Editing

Directions: Choose the letter of the best way to write each underlined section. If the underlined section needs no change, choose "Correct as is." Mark the letter of your answer on a bubble sheet if your teacher provides one; otherwise, number from 1 to 6 on a separate sheet of paper, and write the letter of the correct answer next to each number.

Mount Rushmore National Memorial is in southwestern South Dakota. It is in the Black Hills
(1)
there. Carved into the rocks there are the heads of four Presidents. They are George
(2)
Washington, Thomas Jefferson, Abraham Lincoln, and Theodore Roosevelt. The four heads are
(3)
big. They are each about sixty feet high. Each head represents a different ideal. They represent
(4)
the nation's founding, political philosophy, preservation, and expansion and conservation. The
(5)
memorial was dedicated in 1925. It was first suggested by Jonah Robinson. Work began on the
(6)
memorial in 1927. Work ended on the memorial in 1941.

---

1 A Mount Rushmore National Memorial is in the Southwest in the Black Hills in South Dakota.
  B Mount Rushmore National Memorial is in the Black Hills of southwestern South Dakota.
  C Mount Rushmore National Memorial there in the Black Hills of southwestern South Dakota.
  D Correct as is

2 F Carved into the rocks there are the heads of Presidents George Washington, Thomas Jefferson, Abraham Lincoln, and Theodore Roosevelt.
  G Carved into the rocks there are the Presidents and their heads: George Washington, Thomas Jefferson, Abraham Lincoln, and Theodore Roosevelt.
  H George Washington, Thomas Jefferson, Abraham Lincoln, and Theodore Roosevelt carved their heads in the rocks there.
  J Correct as is

3 A Each of the four large heads is about sixty feet high.
  B Sixty feet high is about how big each of the heads are.
  C Each of the four heads, sixty feet high, are big.
  D Correct as is

4 F The heads, the nation's founding, political philosophy, preservation, and expansion and conservation are represented.
  G Representing the heads are the nation's founding, political philosophy, preservation, and expansion and conservation.
  H Each head represents an ideal—the nation's founding, political philosophy, preservation, and expansion and conservation.
  J Correct as is

5 A The memorial is what was first suggested by Jonah Robinson who was dedicated in 1925.
  B Jonah Robinson first suggested that the memorial be dedicated in 1925.
  C The memorial, which was first suggested by Jonah Robinson, was dedicated in 1925.
  D Correct as is

6 F Work on the memorial began in 1927 and ended in 1941.
  G Work on the memorial ended in 1941 after having been started in 1927.
  H Work in 1927 on the memorial began to be ended in 1941.
  J Correct as is

Recognizing Appropriate Sentence Construction

Directions: Choose the best way to write each underlined section. If the underlined section needs no changes, choose "Correct as is." Mark the letter of your answer on a bubble sheet if your teacher provides one; otherwise, number from 1 to 6 on a separate sheet of paper, and write the letter of the correct answer next to each number.

Valerie had never been to a county fair before. She visited her cousins in Manson, Iowa. They
(1)   (2)
had always written to her about the fair. She had always wanted to go. She really wanted to see
                                                                          (3)
the 4-H Horse Parade, which usually featured at least six breeds of horses! Her cousins, Tina
                                                                              (4)
and Ronnie, owned two Arabian horses that were beautiful by the name of Shama and Aravind.

Shama was gray Aravind was black. Tina had raised them from the time they were little colts
(5)   (6)
just six months old.

---

1 A Valerie had never been to a county fair. Before she visited her cousins in Manson, Iowa.
B Valerie had never been to a county fair before she visited her cousins in Manson, Iowa.
C Valerie had never been to a county fair before, so she visited her cousins in Manson, Iowa.
D Correct as is

2 F They had always written to her about the fair, but she had always wanted to go.
G They had always written to her about the fair. For she had always wanted to go.
H They had always written to her about the fair, and she had always wanted to go.
J Correct as is

3 A She really wanted to see the 4-H Horse Parade, for it usually featured at least six breeds of horses!
B She really wanted to see the 4-H Horse Parade: it usually featured at least six breeds of horses!
C She really wanted to see the 4-H Horse

Parade, and it usually featured at least six breeds of horses!
D Correct as is

4 F Her cousins, Tina and Ronnie, owned Shama and Aravind two Arabian horses that were beautiful.
G Her cousins, Tina and Ronnie, owned two beautiful Arabian horses named Shama and Aravind.
H Her cousins, Tina and Ronnie, owned two beautiful Arabian horses that were by the name of Shama and Aravind.
J Correct as is

5 A Shama was gray, and Aravind was black.
B Shama was gray, but Aravind was black.
C Shama was gray, Aravind was black.
D Correct as is

6 F Tina had raised them from the time they were little colts. Just six months old.
G Tina had raised them from the time they were little colts, just six months old.
H Tina had raised them from the time they were little colts, and just six months old.
J Correct as is

Recognizing Appropriate Sentence Construction

Directions: Choose the best way to write each underlined section. If the underlined section needs no changes, choose "Correct as is." Mark the letter of your answer on a bubble sheet if your teacher provides one; otherwise, number from 1 to 6 on a separate sheet of paper, and write the letter of the correct answer next to each number.

Valerie arrived in Manson, Iowa. Two days before the county fair started. Her cousins met her
(1)   (2)
at the train station. Her cousins brought her back to the farm to see the horses. When Valerie
(3)
saw that Aravind was limping, she started to worry. She was afraid that Aravind was hurt and
(4)
afraid that Ronnie wouldn't be able to show him in the 4-H Horse Parade and afraid that Tina

wouldn't go if her brother couldn't. Ronnie told her that Aravind had only bruised his hoof, he
(5)
was all right. By wearing hot wraps, Aravind could heal in time for the fair.
(6)

---

1 A Two days before Valerie arrived in Manson, Iowa, the county fair started.
   B Valerie arrived in Manson, Iowa, two days before the county fair started.
   C Valerie arrived in Manson, Iowa, and two days before the county fair started.
   D Correct as is

2 F Her cousins met her at the train station and they took her back to the farm to see the horses.
   G Her cousins, met her at the train station but her cousins took her back to the farm to see the horses.
   H Her cousins met her at the train station and took her back to the farm to see the horses.
   J Correct as is

3 A Valerie saw that Aravind was limping. She started to worry.
   B Valerie saw that Aravind was limping, but she started to worry.
   C When Valerie saw that Aravind was limping. She started to worry.
   D Correct as is

4 F She was afraid that Aravind was hurt, that Ronnie wouldn't be able to show him in

the 4-H Horse Parade, and that Tina wouldn't go if her brother couldn't.
   G She was afraid that Aravind was hurt and that Ronnie wouldn't be able to show him in the 4-H Horse Parade. Also that Tina wouldn't go if her brother couldn't.
   H She was afraid that Aravind was hurt. That Ronnie wouldn't be able to show him in the 4-H Horse Parade. And that Tina wouldn't go if her brother couldn't.
   J Correct as is

5 A Ronnie told her that Aravind had bruised his hoof on a rock, but that he was all right.
   B Ronnie told her that Aravind had only bruised his hoof. He was all right.
   C Ronnie told her that Aravind had only bruised his hoof on a rock, because he was all right.
   D Correct as is

6 F Aravind, by wearing hot wraps, would heal in time for the fair.
   G Aravind would heal in time, by wearing hot wraps, for the fair.
   H Aravind would heal in time for the fair. By wearing hot wraps.
   J Correct as is

Standard English Usage: Verb Tenses

Directions: Read the passage, and choose the letter of the word or group of words that belongs in each space. Mark the letter of your answer on a bubble sheet if your teacher provides one; otherwise, number from 1 to 6 on a separate sheet of paper, and write the letter of the correct answer next to each number.

The weather ___(1)___ to warm up, and Dana had her eye on a new mountain bike. She asked her parents if they ___(2)___ it for her, but they said she should try to earn the money herself. She thought about different ways to make money and ___(3)___ to begin a paper route. Every morning she woke up at six o'clock and, with the help of her mom, delivered thirty-two papers to people in her neighborhood. She ___(4)___ some progress, but she still didn't have enough money for her dream bike. Once school was over, she had more free time, so she ___(5)___ cutting neighbors' lawns to earn some additional money. With this additional job, Dana was able to earn enough for the bike in no time. Now that she has her bike, she ___(6)___ her paper route in half the time!

1 **A** starting
   B was starting
   C is starting
   D starts

2 **F** buy
   G bought
   H will buy
   J would buy

3 **A** decides
   B decided
   C is deciding
   D was deciding

4 **F** makes
   G is making
   H was making
   J will be making

5 **A** to start
   B starting
   C started
   D starts

6 **F** completed
   G had completed
   H could have completed
   J can complete

Standard English Usage: Verb Tenses

Directions: Read the passage, and choose the letter of the word or group of words that belongs in each space. Mark the letter of your answer on a bubble sheet if your teacher provides one; otherwise, number from 1 to 6 on a separate sheet of paper, and write the letter of the correct answer next to each number.

The state science fair is this week. Tomorrow, four students from our school ____(1)____ to Austin to compete against other students from Texas. My brother, Corey, ____(2)____ several weeks on his photosynthesis project. He won second place at the regional fair and ____(3)____ to continue in his success. I ____(4)____ to the science fair last year and had a great time. There, I learned a lot from the projects I saw and ____(5)____ many interesting people. I hope my brother ____(6)____ a similar experience.

---

1 A travel
   B have been traveling
   C traveled
   D will be traveling

2 F has spent
   G will spend
   H spends
   J has been spending

3 A will hope
   B hoped
   C hopes
   D has hoped

4 F go
   G will go
   H went
   J have gone

5 A met
   B have met
   C will meet
   D will be meeting

6 F had
   G will have
   H has had
   J will have had

Standard English Usage: Pronouns

Directions: Read the passage, and choose the letter of the word or group of words that belongs in each space. Mark the letter of your answer on a bubble sheet if your teacher provides one; otherwise, number from 1 to 6 on a separate sheet of paper, and write the letter of the correct answer next to each number.

Sam and _____(1)_____ like to ride the ferry from Tiburon to San Francisco. On school holidays, _____(2)_____ catch the ferry at 8:45. In twenty minutes, _____(3)_____ at the pier in the Embarcadero. Sometimes we walk up Taylor Street to visit _____(4)_____ friends Paul and Ted. _____(5)_____ apartment is close to Fisherman's Wharf, so sometimes _____(6)_____ all walk down there to watch the sea lions.

1 **A** me
   B I
   C my
   D mine

2 **F** our
   G us
   H we're
   J we

3 **A** our
   B us
   C we're
   D we

4 **F** our
   G us
   H we're
   J we

5 **A** They're
   B Their
   C There
   D Theirs

6 **F** our
   G us
   H ours
   J we

Standard English Usage: Pronouns

Directions: Read the passage, and choose the letter of the word or group of words that belongs in each space. Mark the letter of your answer on a bubble sheet if your teacher provides one; otherwise, number from 1 to 6 on a separate sheet of paper, and write the letter of the correct answer next to each number.

One day last spring Sam, Debbie, and I met Paul and Ted in the city and ___(1)___ all took the ferry to Alcatraz Island to see the ruins of the famous prison. I planned to take pictures, but I left ___(2)___ camera on the ferry. Debbie took pictures with ___(3)___ camera, though, and ___(4)___ promised to give me copies. ___(5)___ was upset about losing my camera, but I still enjoyed walking around the island and listening to the Park Ranger talk about some famous escapes from the island. When we got back to the ferry building in San Francisco, I checked the Lost and Found, and there was ___(6)___ camera!

1 **A** our
   B ours
   C we
   D we're

2 **F** mine
   G me
   H I
   J my

3 **A** her
   B his
   C its
   D my

4 **F** him
   G she
   H I
   J me

5 **A** mine
   B me
   C I
   D my

6 **F** mine
   G me
   H I
   J my

Standard English Usage: Agreement

Directions: Identify the underlined word or phrase that contains an error in each of the following sentences. Mark the letter of your answer on a bubble sheet if your teacher provides one; otherwise, number from 1 to 6 on a separate sheet of paper, and write the letter of the correct answer next to each number.

1 Seventeen are the number
   (A)
   of Mr. Nguyen's students
   (B)
   who will be taking art class;
   (C)
   only one is taking home economics.
   (D)
   No error.
   (E)

2 All the members of my family
   (A)   (B)
   loves food cooked on the grill.
   (C)   (D)
   No error.
   (E)

3 Zachary and Justin, the Simpson twins,
   (A)   (B)
   are both lifeguarding
   (C)
   at Kenneth Pool this summer.
   (D)
   No error.
   (E)

4 The sweet smelling pines and the beach
   (A)   (B)
   is why I love living in North Carolina.
   (C)   (D)
   No error.
   (E)

5 The Combined Eastern-Western
   (A)
   Junior High School Orchestra
   (B)
   perform one concert
   (C)
   a month at the Lisner Auditorium.
   (D)
   No error.
   (E)

6 Sleeping and eating are the two activities
   (A)   (B)
   my dogs, Rufus and Freckles, prefers most.
   (C)   (D)
   No error.
   (E)

Standard English Usage: Agreement

Directions: Choose the revised version of each numbered sentence below that eliminates all errors in grammar, usage, and mechanics. Mark the letter of your answer on a bubble sheet if your teacher provides one; otherwise, number from 1 to 6 on a separate sheet of paper, and write the letter of the correct answer next to each number.

1 The home team, the Lions, are ahead by seven.
  A The home teams, the Lions, are ahead by seven.
  B The home team, the Lions, are ahead of the other team by seven points.
  C The Lions are the home team, which are ahead by seven.
  D The home team, the Lions, is ahead by seven.

2 Lateesha, who is one of the best students in the class, are going to Riddley, the science magnet school, in the fall.
  F Lateesha, who is one of the best students in the class, is going to Riddley, the science magnet school, in the fall.
  G Lateesha, who are one of the best students in the class, are going to Riddley, the science magnet school, in the fall.
  H Lateesha, who is one of the best students in the class, are going to Riddley, the science magnet school, in the fall.
  J Lateesha, who were one of the best students in the class, are going to Riddley, the science magnet school, in the fall.

3 This morning, each anchor and reporter were telling the story in the headlines.
  A This morning, each anchor and reporter are telling the story in the headlines.
  B This morning, each anchor and reporter had been telling the story in the headlines.
  C This morning, each anchor and reporter was telling the story in the headlines.
  D This morning, each anchor and reporter would be telling the story in the headlines.

4 Waiting out in the rain for the bus was most of the students from Ms. Himmelmann's class.
  F Waiting out in the rain for the bus was many of the students from Ms. Himmelmann's class.
  G Waiting out in the rain for the bus was mostly students from Ms. Himmelmann's class.
  H Waiting out in the rain for the bus were most of the students from Ms. Himmelmann's class.
  J Waiting out in the rain for the bus were most of Ms. Himmelmann's class.

5 It was Mario, a student at Seven Sisters School, who sing better than anyone else last night.
  A It was Mario, a student at Seven Sisters School, who singed better than anyone else last night.
  B It was Mario, a student at Seven Sisters School, who sang better than anyone else last night.
  C It is Mario, a student at attend Seven Sisters School, who sings better than anyone else last night.
  D It was Mario, a student at Seven Sisters School, whom sing better than anyone else last night.

6 Neither Margaret nor they was in my fifth grade class.
  F Either Margaret or they was in my fifth grade class.
  G Not Margaret nor they were in my fifth grade class.
  H They and Margaret neither was not in my fifth grade class.
  J Neither Margaret nor they were in my fifth grade class.

Using Modifiers

Directions: Read the passage, and choose the letter of the word or group of words that belongs in each space. Mark the letter of your answer on a bubble sheet if your teacher provides one; otherwise, number from 1 to 6 on a separate sheet of paper, and write the letter of the correct answer next to each number.

The precipitation levels in Owensboro, Kentucky, do not vary much. Even so, March tends to be the _____(1)_____ month in the city. October is usually the _____(2)_____ month in Owensboro. For farmers, there's nothing _____(3)_____ than a drought in March, because the crops need the rain to grow.

Farmers in Owensboro grow corn and wheat. However, many agricultural experts believe that soybeans will be the _____(4)_____ crop in Kentucky in the near future. Others, in contrast, think that specialized crops such as watermelons could bring in _____(5)_____ for farmers. Whatever crops farmers grow, agriculture is one of the _____(6)_____ occupations in Kentucky—and the world!

---

1 **A** wetter
   B most wetter
   C wet
   D wettest

2 **F** dry
   G driest
   H dryingest
   J most driest

3 **A** more frightening
   B frighteninger
   C scariest
   D most scary

4 **F** profitablest
   G most profitable
   H more profitable
   J profitable

5 **A** best money
   B even more money
   C even most money
   D bestest money

6 **F** most demanding
   G demandingest
   H more demanding
   J demanding

Using Modifiers

Directions: Read the passage, and choose the letter of the word or group of words that belongs in each space. Mark the letter of your answer on a bubble sheet if your teacher provides one; otherwise, number from 1 to 6 on a separate sheet of paper, and write the letter of the correct answer next to each number.

Coal is Kentucky's ___(1)___ natural resource, even ___(2)___ than wood products. The state has ___(3)___ coal resources—about ninety billion tons! Even so, Wyoming produces ___(4)___ coal on an annual basis than Kentucky. ___(5)___ of the coal produced in Kentucky comes from the eastern region of the state. Pike County is the region's ___(6)___ coal contributor.

---

1 A more important
   B importanter
   C most important
   D importantest

2 F valuabler
   G much valued
   H valuablest
   J more valuable

3 A more enormous
   B enormouser
   C enormous
   D most enormous

4 F many
   G most
   H more
   J much

5 A Most
   B Mostest
   C More
   D Majority

6 F leadingest
   G most leading
   H more leading
   J leading

Proofreading

Directions: Choose the best way to write each underlined section. If the underlined section needs no change, mark the choice "Correct as is." Mark the letter of your answer on a bubble sheet if your teacher provides one; otherwise, number from 1 to 6 on a separate sheet of paper, and write the letter of the correct answer next to each number.

Uncle Loomis, up here!" Hearing me my uncle started walking quickly toward us. "Hurry! It's
(1)   (2)   (3)
730 now, and the show begins at 800!"

I wanted to make sure that we got good seats for my sisters dance performance. Her troupe was
(4)   (5)
going to perform: "Jazz City," "Country-Western House," and "Polka Alley." I had seen the
                                                                              (6)
rehearsal for "Jazz City," and it was my favorite.

---

1 A Uncle Loomis, up here!
B Uncle Loomis, "up here!"
C "Uncle Loomis, up here!"
D Correct as is

2 F Hearing me: my uncle started walking
quickly toward us.
G Hearing me, my uncle started walking
quickly toward us.
H Hearing me—my uncle—started walking
quickly toward us.
J Correct as is

3 A "Hurry! It's 7:30 now, and the show begins
at 8:00!"
B Hurry! It's 730 now, and the show begins
at 800!
C "Hurry. It's 730 now, and the show begins
at 800."
D Correct as is

4 F "I wanted to make sure that we got good
seats for my sisters dance performance."

G I wanted to make sure, that we got good
seats for my sisters' dance performance.
H I wanted to make sure that we got good
seats for my sister's dance performance.
J Correct as is

5 A Her troupe was going to perform "Jazz
City," "Country-Western House," and
"Polka Alley".
B Her troupe was going to perform; "Jazz
City," "Country-Western House," and
"Polka Alley."
C Her troupe was going to perform "Jazz
City," "Country-Western House," and
"Polka Alley."
D Correct as is

6 F I had seen the Rehearsal for "Jazz City,"
and it was my favorite?
G "I had seen the rehearsal for "Jazz City,"
and it was my favorite."
H I had seen, the rehearsal for "Jazz City,"
and it was my favorite.
J Correct as is

Proofreading

Directions: Choose the best way to write each underlined section. If the underlined section needs no change, mark the choice "Correct as is." Mark the letter of your answer on a bubble sheet if your teacher provides one; otherwise, number from 1 to 6 on a separate sheet of paper, and write the letter of the correct answer next to each number.

Mrs Farengold handed out the assignment at the beginning of class Remember, she told us,
(1)   (2)
you've got to do good solid research on the Aztec Indians to get a great grade on this paper.

Glenna asked if we could use the Internet to conduct our research.
(3)
    "Well, Mrs Farengold said, considering the issue, You can, but remember—not all the
(4)
information on the Internet is accurate." Glenna nodded! And told Mrs Farengold about a Web
(5)
site she'd seen that said Christopher Columbus landed in the Caribbean in 1592, not 1492!

That's precisely the problem with the Internet, and some other sources too Mrs Farengold said.
(6)
Remember to use your critical thinking skills?

---

1 A Mrs. Farengold handed out the assignment at the beginning of class.
   B Mrs. Farengold handed out the assignment at the beginning of class
   C Mrs Farengold handed out the assignment, at the beginning of class.
   D Correct as is

2 F "Remember, she told us, you've got to do good solid research on the Aztec Indians to get a great grade on this paper."
   G "Remember, she told us. You've got to do good solid research on the Aztec Indians to get a great grade on this paper?"
   H "Remember," she told us, "you've got to do good, solid research on the Aztec Indians to get a great grade on this paper."
   J Correct as is

3 A Glenna asked, "if we could use the Internet to conduct our research?"
   B Glenna asked, If we could use the Internet to conduct our research?
   C Glenna asked if We could use the Internet to conduct our research.
   D Correct as is

4 F "Well," Mrs. Farengold said, considering the issue, "you can, but remember—not all the information on the Internet is accurate."
   G "Well, Mrs. Farengold" said, considering the issue, "You can, but remember—not all the information on the Internet is accurate!"

H "Well, Mrs Farengold said, considering the issue," "You can, but remember—not all the information on the Internet is accurate."
   J Correct as is

5 A Glenna nodded! And told Mrs Farengold about a Web site she'd seen that said "Christopher Columbus landed in the Caribbean in 1592, not 1492!"
   B Glenna nodded and told Mrs. Farengold about a Web site she'd seen that said Christopher Columbus landed in the Caribbean in 1592, not 1492!
   C Glenna nodded. And told Mrs Farengold about a web site she'd seen that said Christopher Columbus landed in the Caribbean in 1592, not 1492?
   D Correct as is

6 F "That's precisely the problem with the Internet, and some other sources, too," Mrs. Farengold said. "Remember to use your critical thinking skills."
   G "That's precisely the problem with the Internet, and some other sources too Mrs Farengold said. Remember to use your critical thinking skills."
   H "That's precisely the problem with the Internet! And some other sources too!" Mrs Farengold said, "remember to use your critical thinking skills."
   J Correct as is

Proofreading

Directions: Read the passage, and decide which type of error, if any, appears in each underlined section. Mark the letter of your answer on a bubble sheet if your teacher provides one; otherwise, number from 1 to 6 on a separate sheet of paper, and write the letter of the correct answer next to each number.

<u>Mr. Gaspar, the School Librarian,</u> organized a reading contest to raise money for library books.
(1)

The way the contest works is that <u>our parents neighbors and friends</u> pledge a certain amount of
(2)

money for each book we read. <u>All the Money is donated to the school library.</u> <u>I decided that i</u>
(3)   (4)

<u>wanted to raise $100.</u> <u>I collected forty name's on my pledge list.</u> <u>Most of the people promissed</u>
(5)   (5)   (6)

five or ten cents per book. I have to read a lot of books to reach my goal. I had better get started!

---

1   **A** Spelling error
     B Capitalization error
     C Punctuation error
     D No error

2   **F** Spelling error
     G Capitalization error
     H Punctuation error
     J No error

3   **A** Spelling error
     B Capitalization error
     C Punctuation error
     D No error

4   **F** Spelling error
     G Capitalization error
     H Punctuation error
     J No error

5   **A** Spelling error
     B Capitalization error
     C Punctuation error
     D No error

6   **F** Spelling error
     G Capitalization error
     H Punctuation error
     J No error

Proofreading

Directions: Read the passage, and decide which type of error, if any, appears in each underlined section. Mark the letter of your answer on a bubble sheet if your teacher provides one; otherwise, number from 1 to 6 on a separate sheet of paper, and write the letter of the correct answer next to each number.

My great uncle Jonas, lives on a farm outside town. He keeps goats and chickens. and also
(1)   (2)
breeds beagles. My brothers and I like to go out to the farm to visit uncle Jonas. Leon, my
(3)   (4)
youngest brother, will spend hours playing with the puppies. My Cousin Sam likes to play
(5)
washers with Uncle Jonas. I love to play with the goats.
(6)

1 A Spelling error
   B Capitalization error
   C Punctuation error
   D No error

2 F Spelling error
   G Capitalization error
   H Punctuation error
   J No error

3 A Spelling error
   B Capitalization error
   C Punctuation error
   D No error

4 F Spelling error
   G Capitalization error
   H Punctuation error
   J No error

5 A Spelling error
   B Capitalization error
   C Punctuation error
   D No error

6 F Spelling error
   G Capitalization error
   H Punctuation error
   J No error

Interpreting Graphic Aids

Directions: Read the passage and answer the questions that follow. Mark the letter of your answer on a bubble sheet if your teacher provides one; otherwise, number from 1 to 6 on a separate sheet of paper, and write the letter of the correct answer next to each number.

The students at Young Middle School like to get involved. There are many school-sponsored clubs that they can choose to participate in. There was a recent survey in which one hundred students were asked what their favorite club was. The results are outlined in the pie chart below.

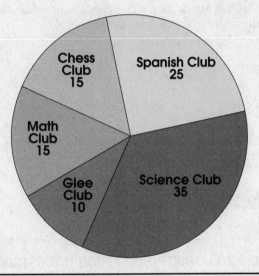

1 How many students chose the Chess Club as their favorite club?
   A 5
   B 10
   C 15
   D 25

2 Which two clubs are the most popular among the students surveyed?
   F Spanish Club and Science Club
   G Science Club and Math Club
   H Math Club and Chess Club
   J Spanish Club and Math Club

3 Of all the clubs mentioned, which was the least popular among the students?
   A Math Club
   B Glee Club
   C Chess Club
   D Spanish Club

4 How many clubs exist at Young Middle School?
   F 4
   G 5
   H 6
   J It cannot be determined from the given information.

5 How many more students chose the Spanish Club over the Chess Club as their favorite club?
   A 5
   B 10
   C 15
   D 20

6 What percentage of the students at Young Middle School chose either the Glee Club or the Math Club as their favorite club?
   F 15
   G 20
   H 25
   J It cannot be determined from the given information.

Name _____   Date _____

Interpreting Graphic Aids

Directions: Read the passage and answer the questions that follow. Mark the letter of your answer on a bubble sheet if your teacher provides one; otherwise, number from 1 to 6 on a separate sheet of paper, and write the letter of the correct answer next to each number.

Stidham Middle School is a school on the move. Its student population has consistently been increasing for the past five years. Administrators at the school expect that this trend will continue. Many families continue to move to this area because of the thriving computer industry here. With the increase in the student population has also come an increase in the number of teachers and staff needed at Stidham Middle School. Portable school buildings have also been added to accommodate all of the additional people at the school.

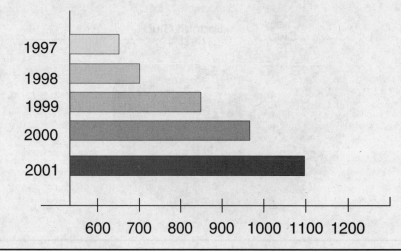

1 How many students attended Stidham Middle School in 1998?
   A 650
   B 700
   C 750
   D 800

2 In what year did Stidham Middle School have the greatest student enrollment?
   F 1998
   G 1999
   H 2000
   J 2001

3 How many more students did Stidham Middle School have in 2001 than in 1997?
   A 450
   B 500
   C 550
   D 600

4 Based on the information you have, what do you think the student population will be like in 2002?
   F There will be fewer students than in 2001.
   G There will be more students than in 2001.

H There will be the same number of students as in 2001.
J It cannot be inferred from this graph.

5 If you were to see a similar graph with the number of teachers at Stidham Middle School each year, what would you expect to see?
   A The number of teachers would be the same for each of these years.
   B The number of teachers would decrease from year to year.
   C The number of teachers would increase from year to year.
   D No conclusions can be made about the number of teachers at Stidham Middle School.

6 If the computer industry in this area were to collapse, what do you think would happen to the student population at Stidham Middle School?
   F There would probably be a slight increase.
   G There would probably be a sharp increase.
   H It would probably decrease or remain constant.
   J It is impossible to tell what would happen to the student population.

Using Context to Determine Word Meaning

Directions: Read the passage. Then, read each question that follows the passage. Decide which is the best answer to each question. Mark the letter of your answer on a bubble sheet if your teacher provides one; otherwise, number from 1 to 6 on a separate sheet of paper, and write the letter of the correct answer next to each number.

The woman sighed and sat down in the chair next to her friend. "I've uncovered some rank doings at work," she said. "They've been hedging on some things for a while, but now I'm pretty sure that I know the truth." The woman's friend asked her what she was going to do about her discoveries. "I am going to the police. I guess the people here are going to label me a whistle-blower," the woman said. She told her friend that she was planning to cushion the blow for her co-workers by warning them in advance. Then she said, "It's late and I'm tired. I have to retire now."

---

1 In this passage, the word rank means—
   A to order according to ability
   B something smelly
   C something wrong
   D a military award

2 In this passage, the word hedging means—
   F confusing the facts
   G spreading out the risks
   H covering all the angles
   J trimming the shrubs

3 In this passage, the word label means—
   A to write something down
   B to give someone an unpleasant name
   C a blank sheet of paper
   D a sticker for a package

4 In this passage, the word whistle-blower means—
   F someone who plays a musical instrument
   G someone who exposes something illegal
   H someone who signals the start of a work shift
   J someone who blows a whistle

5 In this passage, the word cushion means—
   A to protect someone against harm
   B a mattress
   C a pillow
   D to soften bad news

6 In this passage, the word retire means—
   F to stop working altogether
   G to leave a job
   H to go to bed
   J to stay in the house

Using Context to Determine Word Meaning

Directions: Read the passage. Then, read each question that follows the passage. Decide which is the best answer to each question. Mark the letter of your answer on a bubble sheet if your teacher provides one; otherwise, number from 1 to 6 on a separate sheet of paper, and write the letter of the correct answer next to each number.

> After Mr. Wolf hired Ms. Propps to <u>run</u> the debate team, she gave a lecture on different types of arguments. When making a successful argument, she told us, there are several <u>key</u> points to follow. She said that the <u>primary</u> thing was to <u>employ</u> clear, concise arguments. According to Ms. Propps, that simple technique would help us <u>decorate</u> our display case with trophies. Ms. Propps was right. We had a winning season, and Ms. Propps <u>hosted</u> a party to celebrate.

1 In this passage, the word <u>run</u> means—
  A to supervise
  B to force to move quickly
  C to tear sheer fabric
  D to transport

2 In this passage, the word <u>key</u> means—
  F coded
  G related
  H confusing
  J important

3 In this passage, the word <u>primary</u> means—
  A moderately skilled
  B highly important
  C relating to politics
  D first in line

4 In this passage, the word <u>employ</u> means—
  F to give someone a job
  G to put something in order
  H to direct against someone
  J to use something

5 In this passage, the word <u>decorate</u> means—
  A to fill
  B to give a military award
  C to dress up
  D to honor

6 In this passage, the word <u>hosted</u> means—
  F supported
  G served food
  H showed people to seats
  J sponsored

Making Inferences and Predictions

Directions: Read the passage, and then answer the questions that follow. Mark the letter of your answer on a bubble sheet if your teacher provides one; otherwise, number from 1 to 5 on a separate sheet of paper, and write the letter of the correct answer next to each number.

---

from *A Backwoods Boy*, Russell Freedman

    Abraham was growing fast, shooting up like a sunflower, a spindly youngster with big bony hands, unruly black hair, a dark complexion, and luminous gray eyes. He became an expert with the ax, working alongside his father, who also hired him out to work for others. For twenty-five cents a day, the boy dug wells, built pigpens, split fence rails, felled trees. "My how he could chop!" exclaimed a friend. "His ax would flash and bite into a sugar tree or a sycamore, and down it would come. If you heard him felling trees in a clearing, you would say there were three men at work, the way the trees fell."

---

1 The author compares Abraham to a sunflower because—
  A he grows tall quickly
  B he grows tall slowly
  C he is a vine that creeps along the ground
  D he is attractive

2 Why did Abraham's father hire him out to work for others?
  F His father did not want Abraham to get an education.
  G His father did not want to work.
  H The family needed the money Abraham earned.
  J Abraham preferred working to going to school.

3 When Abraham was a boy, twenty-five cents was—
  A worth about the same as it is today
  B worth a lot more than it is today
  C a lot of money for a boy to earn in one day
  D the typical amount of money a man would earn in one day

4 What does Abraham's friend mean when he says, "If you heard him felling trees in a clearing, you would say there were three men at work, the way the trees fell"?
  F Abraham made a lot of noise in the forest.
  G Abraham was not very good at chopping down trees.
  H Abraham spent most of his time in the forest.
  J Abraham chopped many trees down quickly.

5 The narrator is—
  A worried about Abraham
  B embarrassed by Abraham
  C impressed by Abraham's achievements
  D convinced that Abraham's father made a bad decision

Making Inferences and Predictions

Directions: Read the passage, and then answer the questions that follow. Mark the letter of your answer on a bubble sheet if your teacher provides one; otherwise, number from 1 to 5 on a separate sheet of paper, and write the letter of the correct answer next to each number.

> from "Old Ben," by Jesse Stuart
>
> One day early in April I went to the corncrib, and Old Ben lay stretched across the floor. He looked taller than I was now. His skin was rough and his long body had a flabby appearance. I knew Old Ben needed mice and milk. I picked him up, petted him, and told him so. But the chill of early April was still with him. He got his tongue out slower to answer the kind words I was saying to him. He tried to crawl up my arm but he couldn't make it.
>
> That spring and summer mice got scarce in the corncrib and Old Ben got daring. He went over to the barn and crawled up into the hayloft, where he had many feasts. But he made one mistake.

1 The author writes in first person to—
  A increase a feeling of suspense
  B create a contrast between Old Ben and the narrator
  C shock the reader
  D make the details of the story more personal

2 Old Ben is a—
  F snake
  G mythological beast
  H mouse
  J cat

3 It is clear from the passage that the narrator lives—
  A on an Indian reservation
  B in an apartment house in the city
  C on a farm
  D near the ocean

4 Judging from the context of the passage, a corncrib is probably a—
  F baby's bed made of corncobs
  G place where ears of corn are stored
  H restaurant where corn is served
  J traditional item of clothing

5 How does the narrator feel about Old Ben?
  A Old Ben makes the narrator feel sad.
  B Old Ben frightens the narrator.
  C The narrator does not like Old Ben.
  D The narrator is fond of Old Ben.

Constructing Meaning From Informational Texts

Directions: Read the passage. Then, read each question that follows the passage. Decide which is the best answer to each question. Mark the letter of your answer on a bubble sheet if your teacher provides one; otherwise, number from 1 to 6 on a separate sheet of paper, and write the letter of the correct answer next to each number.

Tecumseh was a great Shawnee chief. He was born in 1768 near the present-day city of Springfield, Ohio. Tecumseh's father, Puckeshinwa, was killed in a battle with settlers when Tecumseh was only six. Tecumseh may have disliked settlers in part because he blamed them for his father's death. Tecumseh worked to form a confederacy of Indian tribes to resist European expansion in the Ohio River Valley. In 1812 Tecumseh and his followers joined the British army to fight against the Americans. If Tecumseh had not been killed in battle a year later, the United States would be a very different place today.

1 Which of the following is the main idea of this passage?
 A Tecumseh was a great Shawnee chief.
 B Tecumseh worked to form an Indian confederacy.
 C Tecumseh formed a confederacy of Indian tribes who fought the British army in 1812.
 D If Tecumseh had not been killed, the United States would be a very different place today.

2 Which of the following is an OPINION expressed in the passage?
 F Tecumseh was a great Shawnee chief.
 G Tecumseh was born in 1768.
 H Tecumseh's father, Puckeshinwa, was killed in a battle with settlers.
 J Tecumseh worked to form a confederacy of Indian tribes.

3 Which of the following is a FACT expressed in the passage?
 A Tecumseh was a great Shawnee chief.
 B If Tecumseh had not been killed, the United States would be a very different place today.
 C He was born in 1768 near the present-day city of Springfield, Ohio.
 D Tecumseh blamed settlers for his father's death.

4 Which of the following is the best summary of this passage?
 F Tecumseh was born in 1768 and died in 1813. He fought with the British army and is remembered as having been a great chief.

G Tecumseh was born in 1768. He formed an Indian confederacy to resist settlers. In 1812, Tecumseh joined the British army. He was killed in battle a year later.
 H Tecumseh's father died when he was six. For this reason, Tecumseh disliked settlers and he fought them whenever he could. He even formed a confederacy of Indian tribes to resist them.
 J Tecumseh was a famous Shawnee chief and farmer in the Ohio River Valley. He disliked settlers and formed an Indian confederacy to resist them. In 1812, Tecumseh joined the British army and was killed in battle a year later.

5 Which of the following is an OPINION expressed in the passage?
 A Tecumseh was a great chief, but an inexperienced and ineffective negotiator.
 B The fact that Tecumseh and his father were both killed in battle changed the course of this nation.
 C Tecumseh was a great chief, statesman, and orator.
 D If Tecumseh had not been killed, the United States would be a very different place today.

6 Which of the following can be inferred from the passage?
 F Puckeshinwa died in 1774.
 G Tecumseh's confederacy kept settlers out of the Ohio River Valley.
 H Tecumseh's brothers disliked settlers.
 J If Tecumseh had lived, he would have been elected to Congress.

Constructing Meaning From Informational Texts

Directions: Read the passage. Then, read each question that follows the passage. Decide which is the best answer to each question. Mark the letter of your answer on a bubble sheet if your teacher provides one; otherwise, number from 1 to 6 on a separate sheet of paper, and write the letter of the correct answer next to each number.

> Everyone has heard of Davy Crockett, legendary "king of the wild frontier." It was reported that Crockett swallowed hailstones instead of aspirin to treat a headache, used a pitchfork for a toothpick, and could rip the tail off Halley's Comet. These stories are all tall tales, of course, but David Crockett was a real man who led an exciting and colorful life. He served in the state legislature of Tennessee and was elected to the U.S. Congress three times, and he even considered running for president. Crockett was also famous as a great hunter and humorist.

1 Which of the following is the best summary of this passage?
   A Davy Crockett did not really use a pitchfork for a toothpick, but he was a good hunter and he managed to get elected to Congress three times.
   B Davy Crockett was a colorful figure who wore a coonskin cap and was a great hunter. Crockett was killed defending the Alamo.
   C If people had told the truth about David Crockett, instead of telling tall tales, he might have become president of the United States. Instead, he only served in the U.S. Congress.
   D Many tall tales were written about Davy Crockett, but Crockett did not lead an exciting life. He served in the Tennessee state legislature and was a U.S. congressman.

2 Which of the following is an OPINION expressed in the passage?
   F Crockett swallowed hailstones instead of aspirin to treat a headache.
   G David Crockett served in the state legislature of Tennessee.
   H David Crockett led an exciting and colorful life.
   J Davy Crockett was too humorous to be president.

3 Which of the following is a FACT expressed in the passage?
   A Davy Crockett was elected King of the Wild Frontier.

B Crockett used a pitchfork for a toothpick.
   C Everyone has heard of Davy Crockett.
   D Crockett was elected to the U.S. Congress three times.

4 Which of the following is the main idea of this passage?
   F Crockett was a patriotic American who served his country.
   G The legend of Davy Crockett has come to overshadow the accomplishments of the real man.
   H Davy Crockett, like Paul Bunyan, is a mythological figure of the American frontier.
   J Crockett was the greatest statesman in the history of Tennessee.

5 Which of the following is an OPINION expressed in the passage?
   A The story about Davy Crockett ripping the tail off Halley's Comet is a tall tale.
   B David Crockett was a real man.
   C Everyone has heard of Davy Crockett, legendary "king of the wild frontier."
   D Crockett was famous as a great hunter and humorist.

6 Which of the following can be inferred from the passage?
   F Davy Crockett was fifty at the time of his death.
   G Crockett spent part of his life on the American frontier.
   H Crockett led an exciting and colorful life.
   J Crockett used a rake to comb his hair.

Answers

p. 5
1. C
2. G
3. D
4. H
5. A
6. J

p. 6
1. A
2. H
3. C
4. G
5. B
6. F

p. 11
1. A
2. H
3. A
4. H
5. B
6. J

p. 12
1. A
2. G
3. D
4. F
5. D
6. J

p. 21
1. C
2. H
3. A
4. G
5. A
6. H

p. 22
1. B
2. F
3. C
4. H
5. D
6. H

p. 25
1. B
2. F
3. C
4. J
5. A
6. J

p. 26
1. A
2. G
3. B
4. H
5. A
6. H

p. 27
1. E
2. D
3. A
4. E
5. D
6. C

p. 28
1. E
2. D
3. D
4. E
5. B
6. D

p. 29
1. D
2. G
3. A
4. J
5. D
6. H

p. 30
1. C
2. F
3. D
4. H
5. A
6. J

p. 31
1. B
2. H
3. A
4. J
5. C
6. H

p. 32
1. B
2. F
3. D
4. J
5. B
6. F

p. 33
1. D
2. F
3. B
4. H

p. 34
1. B
2. F
3. C
4. J
5. A
6. H

p. 35
1. C
2. F
3. B
4. J
5. B
6. F

p. 36
1. B
2. H
3. D
4. H
5. B
6. J

p. 37
1. A
2. H
3. A
4. J

p. 38
1. D
2. G
3. A
4. J
5. C
6. G

p. 39
1. C
2. G
3. A
4. F
5. C
6. J

p. 40
1. B
2. F
3. A
4. H
5. C
6. F

p. 41
1. B
2. H
3. D
4. G
5. A
6. G

p. 42
1. B
2. H
3. D
4. F
5. A
6. J

p. 43
1. B
2. J
3. B
4. H
5. C
6. J

p. 44
1. D
2. F
3. C
4. H
5. A
6. G

p. 45
1. B
2. J
3. C
4. F
5. B
6. J

p. 46
1. C
2. J
3. A
4. G
5. C
6. J

p. 47
1. A
2. C
3. E
4. C
5. C
6. D

p. 48
1. D
2. F
3. C
4. H
5. B
6. J

p. 49
1. D
2. G
3. A
4. G
5. B
6. F

p. 50
1. C
2. J
3. C
4. H
5. A
6. J

p. 51
1. C
2. G
3. A
4. H
5. C
6. J

p. 52
1. A
2. H
3. D
4. F
5. B
6. F

p. 53
1. B
2. H
3. B
4. G
5. C
6. F

p. 54
1. C
2. H
3. B
4. J
5. B
6. J

p. 55	p. 57	p. 59	p. 61
1. C	1. C	1. A	1. A
2. F	2. F	2. H	2. F
3. B	3. B	3. B	3. C
4. J	4. G	4. J	4. G
5. B	5. D	5. C	5. D
6. J	6. H		6. F

p. 56	p. 58	p. 60	p. 62
1. B	1. A	1. D	1. A
2. J	2. J	2. F	2. H
3. A	3. B	3. C	3. D
4. G	4. J	4. G	4. G
5. C	5. A	5. D	5. C
6. H	6. J		6. G

To score student responses to the writing prompts presented in this book, use the following rubric.

Scoring Rubric

0	1	2	3	4
Blank paper	Vague or brief	Correct purpose, audience, and mode	Correct purpose, audience, and mode	Correct purpose, audience, and mode
In a foreign language	Wrong purpose, audience, or mode	Organization has lapses	Fair organization	Logical, effective organization
Unreadable because of incoherence or illegilibity	Poorly organized	Some elaboration and detail	Moderate elaboration and detail	Full, appropriate elaboration
On wrong topic	Lacks elaboration; loses focus; rambles	Language control is limited	Clear, effective language	Fluent, clear, effective language
Content too scant to score	Lacks language control			